'No, love,' Paul murmured, voice hoarse with thwarted desire, 'tomorrow you would hate me and I couldn't take that. And, listen, I don't want you to get hurt.' He held Shanna still. 'It's the magic, that's all. It's the magic of Tago Mago.'

They began to walk slowly back up the deserted beach towards the villa. The stark fact was that the moment was approaching when he would turn and say goodnight, goodbye, and she was scarcely aware of the soft words whispered in her ear, the meaning of which lit a spark of hope when once she heeded them.

'And that's a promise,' he murmured as he bent to caress her cheek. 'But I doubt whether you'll thank me for keeping it.'

'We shall meet again?' she repeated in bewilderment. 'A promise?' Her heart fluttered with hope, despite his strange warning.

'We'll meet again, my love. Trust me. Trust in me, whatever happens.'

Another book you will enjoy
by SALLY HEYWOOD

FANTASY LOVER

Torrin Anthony's arrival in Merril's life was unwanted and upsetting, for this shallow and artificial actor reminded her of the heroic Azur—who had rescued her from crossfire in the Middle East.

TODAY, TOMORROW AND FOREVER

BY

SALLY HEYWOOD

MILLS & BOON LIMITED
ETON HOUSE   18-24 PARADISE ROAD
RICHMOND   SURREY   TW9 1SR

First published in Great Britain 1989
by Mills & Boon Limited

© Sally Heywood 1989

Australian copyright 1989
Philippine copyright 1989
This edition 1989

ISBN 0 263 76283 1

Set in Baskerville 12 on 12 pt.
01 – 8904 – 42566

Typeset in Great Britain by JCL Graphics, Bristol

Made and Printed in Great Britain

CHAPTER ONE

'SHANNA! Are you still in the bathroom?'

A muffled reply came from within, and seconds later a dark, curly head popped round the edge of the door. 'Sorry, Dee. Won't be long now.'

'Honestly, does it matter what you look like? He'll be eighty if he's a day, and past caring!' Dee laughed as she went back into the kitchen and disposed of Shanna's now cold cup of coffee. She was making a fresh pot when her cousin at last showed her face.

'Will I do?' She gave a little twirl to show off her suit. The skirt was the new length and showed off her shapely legs to perfection.

'Black stockings?'

'Ritzy enough?'

'He'll have apoplexy!'

Shanna's pert face shone with anticipation as she put her head on one side to judge her cousin's reaction.

'Very ritzy, love,' judged Dee at last, 'and I like the little hat, too. I've never seen you in a hat before.' She eyed the tiny scrap of silk and feathers with the antique silver clip holding it in place. 'You've got a hat face,' she added in surprise.

'Thanks! Whatever that's supposed to mean! Honestly, Dee,' Shanna went on in a different tone, 'I'm scared silly. The Ritz itself, for heaven's sake! Should I take the gloves or not?'

'Yes. We've already gone into that. Carry them. Now get a move on or you'll be late. Here, do you still want this coffee?'

While Shanna hurriedly gulped it down, Dee fussed around her younger cousin, making sure she had the essentials, and when the sound of the taxi came from down below, she shepherded her to the door with strict instructions on how to behave. 'No giggling and no running up or down stairs. Be cool, ladylike—and Shanna——' her face softened, 'don't be too disappointed if all she's left you is a tin brooch.'

'Silly, I'd be overwhelmed if she left me that much! It's the thought, isn't it? I mean, I hardly knew her. Just think,' she paused at the top of the stairs, 'I was three the last time we met. And she was old even then.'

'Everyone over five seems old when you're that age.'

'No, really, she must have been in her seventies!'

The taxi honked its horn down below, and Shanna turned with a happy shake of her head. 'Be here when I get back!'

'Curiosity will keep me riveted to my chair,' called Dee after the retreating figure. She watched, fearing the worst, as Shanna clacked downstairs on the spiky high heels of her black patent court shoes, then gave a sigh of relief as she successfully reached the ground floor.

Shanna, with a darting glance at the sky, hurried to the waiting taxi, then, taking a deep breath, said the words she'd been longing to say ever since she got the invitation.

'To the Ritz, driver, please!'

Then she settled back in the deep leather seat with a little smile. It was lovely to play-act sometimes, and as the taxi sped along she arranged her black-stockinged legs as elegantly as she could and imagined she was being driven to some secret assignation.

Dee was probably right, she thought philosophically, as the cab reached Mayfair. Great-Aunt Vi had probably left her some little trinket as a memento. After all, she had only been her mother's first husband's aunt, not a blood relative at all, though she remembered she had been especially fond of Mother.

A well-known travel writer in her heyday, Aunty Vi had led a scandalous sort of existence, only settling back in Europe in her seventies, and living on a remote island in the Mediterranean until her recent death.

'It's little more than a rock, my dear,' she had once written to Shanna in one of her infrequent though long and newsy letters. And now Shanna regretted never having really got to know her. Somehow, what with school, and the fact that Vi's niece by marriage, Shanna's own

mother, had died some years ago, it had been
outside her orbit to think of planning the long
and difficult journey to Tago Mago. Never
having travelled abroad much except for the
odd package holiday with a group of friends, she
wouldn't have known how to start, and it
seemed too far just to go and see someone she
hardly knew. She had always looked forward to
Vi's letters though.

Now the cab was stuck in a traffic jam on
Piccadilly, and Shanna drummed her fingers
with impatience. Should she get out and walk,
or would it be undignified to arrive at a place
like the Ritz on foot? She decided to sit it out. It
would be fun to arrive in style.

In her first job with the fashion department of
a large West End store after a bumpy spell of
unemployment straight after school, Shanna
had been in a quandary when she first heard
that Aunty Vi was ill.

'I wonder if she's able to cope?' she had asked
Dee with a worried frown. 'I expect she has
plenty of friends out there. I know she's had
innumerable husbands.'

'Is there one now?' Dee had asked, fascinated
by the snippets of information Shanna had fed
her over the years about this scandalous aunt
from the other side of their rambling family.

'One or two, no doubt,' Shanna had laughed.
'I think there will be. I really can't remember!'

In any event, it had been too late to do
anything. News of her death had followed

swiftly. She had been eighty-eight.

With a lurch the cab nosed into the inside lane and came to a halt outside the main entrance of the hotel. The invitation to take afternoon tea in order to discuss certain matters, as it was put, had followed swiftly on the letter informing her of her aunt's death. The letter came from one of the executors, and why he had suggested meeting her before the reading of the will she couldn't imagine.

Details concerning the invitation had been left in the hands of Lionel Metcalf's secretary in his London office, and Shanna got the impression that Mr Metcalf was 'something in the city'.

'A Big Bang whizz-kid?' suggested Dee hopefully, knowing Shanna's own prospects were nil. 'You could do with that!'

'Nonsense, I'm not interested in getting married, and certainly not for money!' They had speculated long and hard over mugs of cocoa about the likelihood of his being young, rich and handsome, finally coming down on the side of common sense when they agreed that any colleague of aged Aunt Vi must himself be pretty ancient too.

'Still, tea at the Ritz! That doesn't happen every day!' exclaimed Shanna in excited anticipation.

Now she felt nervous as she walked in through the revolving doors and gazed round the sumptuous foyer, trying to pretend she knew where she was going.

An old gentleman in a three-piece black suit and carrying a highly polished leather briefcase made his way towards her.

'My dear, you must be Shanna Douglas?' He referred to a photograph Shanna remembered sending to Aunt Vi the previous Christmas. She thought it made her look prettier than she really was. But Mr Metcalf held out his hand, skin cracking like old parchment as he smiled a greeting.

'My,' he exclaimed, as he led her towards the dining-room, 'you're far younger than I'd envisaged, despite the photograph! And all the more reason for having a chat before meeting the solicitors. Decisions, decisions!' he added mysteriously as he led her to a table for two overlooking the park.

There, over Earl Grey and finger sandwiches served on the thinnest of bone china, he began to outline the reasons for wanting to see her.

'It's no secret, my dear. Your great-aunt has left you one of her villas——' he consulted a document beside him on the table '—the Villa Mimosa, together with that part and parcel of land known as Tago Mago. That's the island,' he looked at her over the top of his spectacles, 'on which it stands. The whole to be shared equally with one Richard Mather,' he glanced at his documents again, 'only son of a friend now deceased—the friend, that is,' he added in case there should be any misunderstanding. 'The bulk of the estate, of course, goes to close family.'

'Estate?' Shanna rubbed a hand across her forehead.

'Your great-aunt was a very rich woman,' he reproved.

'And she's left me an island? In her will?' Shanna wondered if she sounded as stupid as she felt.

Mr Metcalf smiled benignly, as if used to the confusion his pronouncements wrought, and went on, 'The island is, as you no doubt know, rather remote and of little commercial interest, being unsuitable for development; however, I have some excellent news for you in that regard.' He pressed his finger-tips together and looked pleased with himself. 'I'm pleased to be able to tell you that an offer has already been made for the freehold——'

'Offer?'

'Someone would like to purchase it, my dear,' he explained gently.

'Sorry I'm being so dim.' Shanna rubbed a finger against her right temple and struggled to come to terms with the simple fact that she was now the owner of a Mediterranean island. Part-owner, she corrected, thoughts blurring as she tried to imagine what this would mean. What on earth was she going to do with an island? Live on it? But what about her job? What about her flat with Dee in London?

'And you say somebody wants to buy it?' she repeated. Her blue eyes widened. 'But why should they? I thought you said it was of little commercial interest?'

'So it is, my dear,' Mr Metcalf's eyes narrowed briefly, and he gave a hurried glance at his fob watch. 'It happens to be an excellent offer, giving you a substantial lump sum which you could then invest—or use to purchase a more suitable property for yourself, perhaps even here in London.'

Shanna gave a hollow laugh. 'It must be a good offer,' she remarked, before asking carefully, 'I'm to understand you're advising me to accept?' When he nodded, she went on, 'Before I've even seen the place?'

He nodded again, this time more doubtfully.

She raised her pert face and gave him a searching little smile. 'And what would Aunty Vi think to that, I wonder?'

'It's all so obviously wrong!' she exclaimed later to Dee. 'Why are they hassling me to sell? Surely this tycoon, whoever he is, can wait a few weeks until I've had chance to look it over? Who knows, I may fall for the place and decide to keep it!'

'Yes, I can imagine you as a castaway, dear Shanna. You'd curl up and die from sheer loneliness in sixty minutes flat!'

'I shan't always want to bubble around the social scene, you know. People do change!'

'Not that much!'

'Well, anyway, I want to see this Tango Mago,' she replied stubbornly. 'Even the name has a mysterious ring! I must go there, Dee, don't you understand?' Her face sobered. 'I must

confess I feel a little bit guilty that Aunty Vi
decided to be so generous when I never made
any effort to visit her——'

'I thought she jetted in and out of London all
the time?' Dee reminded her.

'Yes, and she was always too busy, I grant
you. Very well. I don't feel guilty exactly. But I
still think I ought to go over there and sort of pay
my respects to the place and to her memory.' She
shrugged. 'It would seem wrong to let the
solicitors deal with it all.' She threw back her
head. 'It's mine, Dee! All mine! My very own
island!'

'Yours and this Richard Mather's,' Dee
reminded.

They had already discussed Shanna's co-
owner at length, but, having little to go on, were
as much in the dark as ever. So far, all they knew
was what the solicitors had told her, and as they
had been unable to locate him it wasn't much. A
traveller like Aunty Vi, he had last been heard of
in the Malay peninsula.

'So I can't sell up, anyway, not until he comes
back?' she had asked.

'We hope to get a power of attorney as soon as
we've contacted him. He needn't come back at
all,' was the reply.

'But you expect him to want to sell?' she had
persisted.

The solicitor nodded in agreement.

She gave Dee a doubtful look now, and two
fine lines creased her forehead. 'Doesn't it seem

odd to you, Dee? In the first place, what made Aunty Vi bequeath such a place to us? And why us? What did she expect us to do with it? And then again,' she wrinkled her brow, 'why should anybody want to make an offer for a place that sounds so unattractive?'

'It can't be all that bad. Your aunt lived there for years. And if she was as wealthy as they make out, she could have had her pick of locations.'

'True. But these people, whoever they are, seem willing to offer over the odds for it according to Metcalf. I won't get a better offer,' she mimicked.

Still sure she wanted to go and see for herself, Shanna arranged to take a week off work and got down to the serious business of booking flights. It was then she hit the problems.

'Remote isn't in it, the place is positively inaccessible! Do you know, I'm going to have to fly to Malaga, take a ferry to the main island, then get a bus or car to a town in the north and then——' she paused dramatically, 'then I have to take a taxi to a dot on the coast opposite the island itself? At that point I'm supposed to engage the services of a local fisherman to take me over, either that or, if I'm lucky, get the once-a-week mail-boat.' She raised her eyebrows. 'How does that sound?'

'As you say, inaccessible.' Dee shook her head. 'Honestly, Shanna, you ought to think twice.'

'I've thought twice and the answer's still yes.'
She jutted her chin. 'It only makes me all the
more determined.'

Four hectic days later, Shanna found herself in
a small town on the less inhabited side of the
island, where she had fully expected to be able
to hire a taxi to take her to the right bit of coast
for the final leg of her journey. However, she
had reckoned without the holiday season. In the
middle of summer Santa Eulalia was a thriving
resort, with taxis aplenty, but in the middle of
November it was quite a different situation, and
now the whole place had the air of a ghost town.

Dropped at the bus stop in the market square,
she gazed helplessly from side to side, wondering where to start next. A short circumnavi-
gation of the square brought her back to her
starting point without having found any
solution. All the shop fronts were boarded up,
and she looked round desperately, wondering
what to do next.

Spying a café down one of the side roads
leading off the square, Shanna hoisted her bag
back on to her shoulder, glad she was travelling
light, and headed towards it. Although its tables
were empty under a draggled awning of autum-
nal wistaria, she decided it offered the only
prospect of help. Optimistically she made her
way across the road.

There was only one other customer, a tourist
like herself, she guessed, noting the blond hair

and casual all-in-white get-up. He was reading a paper and didn't look up as she wove her way between the empty chairs to the back of the café in search of the owner.

She found a large, sullen-looking woman behind a counter polishing glasses, but when she asked if there was a taxi available all she got was a shrug of the shoulders.

Slightly miffed, she repeated the question in her best phrase-book Spanish, but the woman merely shrugged again and replied, 'Taxi kaput,' shaking her head vigorously from side to side in confirmation.

'But I have to get to a place called Cala Longa!' exploded Shanna in English.

The woman gave her a look of incomprehension that sent Shanna outside again. Maybe it had been crazy to ignore everybody's advice and turn up here without making any proper arrangements. But surely there was a solution to the problem? She stood undecidedly among the empty chairs and tables.

'Problems?' asked a voice from beside her. She gave a start. The stranger had folded his newspaper and was giving her a level glance as she stood looking helplessly round.

'Thank heavens! Somebody who speaks English!' she exclaimed. 'I don't know whether it's my phrase-book Spanish or what, but I don't seem to be able to make myself understood. There must be a taxi in the town, surely?' The words came pouring out. She explained, 'I haven't talked to a soul since I set off. I was beginning to think I'd forget how to talk! Are you on holiday?' she asked, pausing.

The stranger didn't reply, merely giving a sudden smile, bright blue eyes lazing over her in an unexpectedly thorough assessment that made her painfully aware how dishevelled she must look after hours in a rickety bus.

'I've been travelling for ever!' she exclaimed.

He gave her a wide smile in sympathy. 'It must suit you. Come and join me and tell me what's gone wrong.'

'It's that woman inside,' she confided, lowering her voice as soon as she was sitting down opposite him, 'she was so unfriendly. I was only trying to ask for a taxi.'

'Maybe she didn't understand?'

'Maybe. I wish I could speak the language,' she said feelingly. 'Anyway,' she went on, 'I refuse to believe there isn't a taxi. There must be! I've simply *got* to get to Cala Longa.'

'Staying in one of the villas, I suppose? I must say you've chosen a strange time of year. Everything's shut.'

'So I've noticed. But no, I'm not staying in one, though I hope I'll be able to find one for tonight.' She looked worried and bit her lip. 'This is far more difficult than I imagined it was going to be.'

'Can I help?'

'Only if you can conjure a taxi out of thin air,' she smiled.

'I expect I can do that. It's a simple enough trick once you know where he happens to be having his siesta.'

'And you do?' She felt a wave of relief gush through her. 'You heavenly man!' Her eyes sparkled with mischief, and she had to stop herself from throwing her arms right round his neck.

Then she gave him a proper look. It was his appearance that stopped her from doing anything so outrageous—not that he was ugly, just the opposite, in fact—he was too good-looking! Breathtaking. She felt her lips part. She would have to report back properly to Dee. She would never believe her.

Mediterranean eyes, she would say, blue, deep blue, and hair a wild, natural, sunstreaked blond; a tough, lean face, strong jaw, enough lines to give him character, but not too many to put him at more than thirty, and then—she gulped—a physique to match his looks.

It wasn't fair! Heavenly broad shoulders, the build of an athlete, and surely, when he eventually stood up, he would be tall, with those long, long legs in their white cricketing trousers. Heavens, he had it all——

'Sorry?' She blushed furiously. He had actually asked her a question, and she had been so taken up by the way he looked that she hadn't even heard!

'I said, would you like me to get you a cup of coffee?'

'Sorry, I still feel as if I'm sitting on that old bus.' She grinned up at him, recovering her composure at once. 'There's nothing I would like better. Make it black, no sugar.'

Somehow he seemed to cause the proprietor to materialise, smiling, from behind the counter, and soon a cup of the very best and blackest hot coffee, together with a plate of *brioches* oozing butter were placed before her.

'You're a magician,' she remarked. 'If I'd tried that I'd probably have finished up with lamb chops.'

He laughed aloud. 'You'll have to mime everything. You've got the face!'

She wrinkled her nose. 'And what's that supposed to mean?'

He didn't answer, but went on, 'What on earth made you come out here at this time of year? You must have a real yen to get away from it all!'

Shanna pulled another face. 'I might ask you the same question,' she told him, giving him an opening to tell her something about himself, but he merely grinned at her, making her scowl. On closer inspection he didn't look at all like a tourist, but more as if he'd taken a long lease on the whole town.

His high-handedness acted as a provocation, but before she could think up a reply he went on, 'You must have come in on the night flight?'

'How do you know?' she demanded.

'Didn't you?'

'I did, as it happens——'

'Most people do if they intend to get the bi-weekly bus out here,' he explained, confounding her by modestly disclaiming any special knowledge, 'not much point in hanging around in the main town out of season unless you happen to live here.'

He was watching her with an amused expression, and it made her toss her head with a gesture of annoyance. 'What else do you deduce, Monsieur Poirot?' she mocked.

'You're about twenty, single, work in fashion or publicity or something like that, and——' he paused '—if you're hoping for some disco action you're in for a big disappointment. Come back in August.'

She gave him a sardonic glance, lips slightly parted.

'Am I right?'

'Maybe.' She shrugged, annoyed that he had read her so accurately. 'Not entirely, though.' At least he didn't know *why* she was here. And, given his arrogance, she would keep that to herself! 'Do I look the disco type?' she asked with a level glance.

His blue eyes trailed deliberately over her slim form in white cotton trousers and skimpy T-shirt, and by the time it returned to her face she felt she had been thoroughly stripped. Fighting back her blushes, she said coolly, 'Obviously your answer's yes.' Let him think

what he likes, she thought furiously. Who in hell
is he to sit there looking me over as if he's some
sort of Spanish *señor* with feudal rights he fully
intends to claim? She blushed at the thought,
honest enough to realise that it owed as much to
her own wishful thinking as to the blazing
provocation of his own raking scrutiny.

Angry with herself for letting her feelings get
so out of hand, she began to fish around for her
phrase-book in the capacious black travel-bag at
her feet.

When she managed to drag it out, he took it
from her hands before she had time to open it.
'I'm sorry.' He didn't need to explain why.
Looking at his watch, he said, 'I suppose you
were hoping to stay overnight in Cala Longa
and get a boat out to the island tomorrow?'

She nodded, feeling confused by the swift
change from open sexual appraisal to this brisk
efficiency.

'Not a hope, I'm afraid. You obviously
haven't done your homework properly. Cala
Longa is nothing but a beach bar together with
about fifty brightly coloured parasols—and
that's in the high season.'

'But I thought it was a fishing village. There
must be boats——' she protested.

'There are four houses on the clifftop, once
owned by local fishermen, but, like all the rest
of the houses up here these days, they now
belong to summer residents.'

'So how on earth am I to get out to the

island?' In the light of this new obstacle, finding somewhere to stay seemed the least of her worries.

'There is a chap who might help out if he's not worrying about the olive harvest or whether his hens are laying this morning, or if there's an ''r'' in the month,' he grinned disarmingly.

'It's no joke!' she protested. 'And I'll pay——'

'That probably won't have much bearing on the issue.'

'But where on earth am I going to stay?' Shanna bit her lip, taking in the full implications of her predicament. Despite her mixed feelings about this man he was her only life line and she had a sense of throwing herself on his mercy.

'First things first.' He put some coins on the table beside his empty coffee-cup and stood up. 'Look, while you're tucking into that I'll go and fix a cab for you. There is only one, and I'm sure it's not booked.' With another of those wide, white smiles like the one with which he had first greeted her, he made his way between the tables. 'Don't go anywhere. It may take a few minutes,' he called back.

After he'd gone, Shanna looked round. Not much chance of going anywhere! And with the prospect of such a gorgeous-looking man coming back to fetch her, going anywhere was the last thing she was likely to be doing!

Eagerly looking out for him, she soon heard
the noise of a car engine, followed by the sight of
a rapidly driven orange cab. It was quite
battered and Shanna would have feared for the
proficiency of the driver and her own safety at
any other time. Now, however, she felt only
relief. At least she could push on with the next
stage of her journey.

The stranger who had gone to fetch the taxi
climbed out of the front passenger seat and
opened a rear door, throwing in her leather bag
and indicating that she should climb in after it.

She was relieved to see that he intended to
come with them, and as he resumed his seat
beside the driver the cab lurched forward and
they were soon bowling along the coast road
with the sea sparkling to one side.

Shanna heard the name Cala Longa, and a
little later something that might have been Tago
Mago, but she couldn't make head nor tail of
what else was being said and, seeing how well
her rescuer seemed to be handling things, she
sat back and began to enjoy herself.

The twenty-minute journey gave her a
chance to speculate about him in more detail.
He really seemed at home here. Fluent in
Spanish, he could have passed for a local
businessman but for the bright hair and blue eyes,
and she wondered what he was doing out here.
He hadn't denied that he was on holiday, but he
hadn't admitted it either, and, now she thought
about it, he didn't look like an average British

holiday-maker either. He didn't look like an average anything.

For one thing, he was so chic. Really cosmopolitan. His suit cut just right. His shoes casual but obviously beautifully made. He was probably the type to speak about ten languages and have homes in several continents, Shanna thought, wondering what it was he did for a living. She let her imagination run riot, shamelessly imagining him as a film star, taking a short, reclusive holiday away from the gaping crowds perhaps, or as a famous writer, plotting his next best-seller in the charm and seclusion of this out-of-the-way spot.

She laughed at herself. He was probably a villain, dodging the police of three continents, and she was a fool to trust him.

Surprised at herself for putting herself so completely in his hands, she pondered the pros and cons. She supposed she could handle most situations, *ingénue* traveller though she was.

Soon they were pulling up outside a large villa at the top of a narrow lane. As the car door opened, she could hear the breaking of waves on a not too distant beach and, following her glance, the cab driver smiled and pointed, saying, *'El mar,'* and making swimming movements with his hands.

She nodded and smiled back, feeling like a fool again because she couldn't communicate properly. But it didn't matter, for he nodded, adding, 'Cala Longa.'

In a moment a woman came to the steps of the villa and the Englishman called out to her in Spanish, apparently explaining. She nodded, gave Shanna a brief smile, and went back inside, obviously meaning for them to follow her.

Shanna began to fish around in her shoulder-bag for her currency to pay off the taxi, but the Englishman came back, waving her aside. 'Let me handle it. I had to visit people out here and it means I've simply arrived a little earlier than anticipated.'

'No, really, I——'

'Please. I'm not just being polite.'

I can believe that, thought Shanna silently. Despite his dazzle of a smile and his air of charm, she could imagine his courtesy came from natural feelings, not from the wish to fit into conventional models of polite behaviour. She could imagine he'd be very abrupt if he wanted to be.

She waited while he gave the cab driver some notes, and with much smiling the man drove off back to town.

'You can stay here overnight. Luisa is a friend of mine and runs this as a holiday villa in the season. There's always room at this time of year. Come inside and have a rest. I shall return before dinner with a boat trip organised for tomorrow morning.'

'Quite a Mr Fix-it, aren't you?' Shanna couldn't help remarking, taken aback by the man's self-confident handling of events.

He laughed aloud and the blue eyes flashed as they met hers. 'Coming from any other lips but yours, I would take that as a very back-handed compliment.'

'How do you know it wasn't intended as such?' she sparked back.

'Ingratitude from lips like yours—never!' he said at once in a voice like velvet. He raised one hand and for a moment she thought he was going to reach out and touch the lips he'd just remarked on, but, apparently thinking better of it, he spun on his heel and strode up the steps into the house.

Used to getting in the last word, Shanna watched him disappear with a muttered exclamation, only following him when he vanished from view. He had her bag. If for no other reason, she hurried after him.

CHAPTER TWO

AFTER he had gone, leaving her in the hands of the housekeeper, Shanna looked round the room she had been given, noting the pretty flowered duvet, the simple furnishings, the grey marbled floor and blue shutters now standing open. It was simply furnished but spotlessly clean.

Luisa evidently spoke no English, for after showing her where the bathroom was and how to open and shut the wardrobe, she had disappeared downstairs without another word. Feeling much like an abandoned parcel, Shanna was now alone.

And I don't even know his name, she realised, thoughts flying back to her rescuer once more. Opening her bag, she took out a clean towel and sponge-bag. At least she could make use of the private shower, put on a change of clothes and try to regain a stake in this game of guess what happens next. She had never felt so helpless. Lucky for her someone had appeared on the scene to sort things out! She would have to get over her crossness at feeling so deeply in his debt.

True to his promise, he walked up the drive just before dinner. The unaccustomed heat had forced Shanna out on to the terrace, and she was sitting by herself sipping an aperitif when she saw the gleam of his white jacket through the dusk. He came straight across to her.

'Everything all right?' he greeted her.

'Apart from the fact that it's like a ghost house with no one else staying, yes,' she replied shortly, and in case that sounded ungrateful she added, 'It seems strange to be travelling alone. I'm not really used to it. And I'm certainly not used to places like this out of season. I can't get over the fact that I'm the only person here.'

'We may find the weather warm enough, but the locals regard this as the beginning of winter.'

'It's like an English summer evening,' she smiled. 'In fact, better—I don't need a raincoat!' She paused. 'I'm sorry if I sounded ungrateful just now. You've really saved my bacon. It's just that I hate to feel I've made such a hash of things.'

'You haven't made a hash—on the contrary, you've succeeded in doing exactly what you set out to do. Or at least, by tomorrow you will have if you follow my instructions.'

'Oh?'

He sat down opposite. 'Your boat to the island will be ready when you are after breakfast. I suggest you try to make it about nine o'clock.'

'Where do I meet it?' she asked.

'At the beach. Just follow the road you saw when we arrived. In fact,' he suggested, 'we might take a walk that way after dinner if it isn't too dark.' He paused. 'You don't mind if I join you, do you?' Before she had time to answer he went on, 'Or do you have something else planned?'

'Like a disco, you mean?' She gave him a teasing smile from beneath her lashes and was disconcerted to find his glance, direct and amused, answering straight to her own. It was like an open caress. She blushed before she could stop herself. He had the most sexy eyes. They were pretty sharp, too, weighing every nuance of expression. It would be hell to try to conceal anything from someone like this. Not that she could imagine ever wanting to do so.

'I'll see what kind of entertainment I can lay on for you,' he murmured suggestively.

'It's all right,' she exclaimed, confused, 'you've already done such a lot for me. I feel like an early night actually——' She broke off when she realised what she'd said.

But he didn't take her up on it or tease her any more. 'Look, we don't even know each other's names,' he said briskly. 'I'm Paul Elliot.' He held out a hand.

Gingerly reaching for it, she replied, 'Shanna Douglas,' snatching her hand away as soon as it touched his.

'By the look of alarm on your face, you're having second thoughts about me,' he remarked casually, breaking off a piece of bread from the pieces piled in a straw basket. 'I'm quite harmless really.'

'It all depends on what you mean by harmless,' she joked, regaining her composure. He really was all right. She knew she could trust her intuition.

There was an amused quirk to his lips. 'Somebody harmless is one who keeps a sensible distance,' he told her.

She wanted to ask, Do you have to? but knew it would lead at once into deeper waters. She drew back, only saying lightly, 'I can trust you to do that, I'm sure.' Perhaps he has an involvement already, she thought. A man like this is bound to be taken! Even now he's probably thinking about the woman he's going back home to tonight after our meal, somebody in Santa Eulalia perhaps.

'Are you staying here long?' she asked, injecting a light, uninvolved tone into the conversation herself.

He gave her an odd look. 'Possibly.' He didn't go on to explain.

'I expect some hotels stay open all the year round?'

'Some, not many,' he agreed, as if he didn't know it was a indirect way of asking him something about himself. He was so reticent that for a brief moment she felt he was hiding something. It made her feel as if she was being nosy when it was really just a way of making conversation. Or nearly so. She couldn't help admitting she'd like to know a lot more about him, but she wasn't prying and didn't like to feel he might think she was.

He got up and went towards the kitchens and

she watched as he leaned familiarly in through the open window to speak to someone inside. When he came back he was carrying a dish of *aeoili* and a carafe of wine.

'This should keep the midges away,' he remarked. 'The rule is,' he indicated the dish, 'all diners eat it, or none.'

'All, then,' she said at once, eager to try anything new. She copied the way he dipped a piece of bread into it, tasting it with her eyes shut. 'Heavenly!' she declared. 'I must learn to pronounce it properly so I can ask for it again!'

'I've never seen anyone look so blissful over something so simple,' he remarked, laughing. 'Are you always so easy to please?'

'Over some things,' she replied. 'Over other things I'm difficult beyond belief.'

'Such as?'

She frowned. Her impulse was to say 'men'—Dee was always telling her she was too choosy—but she hesitated, afraid of what it might provoke.

'Come on, no cheating,' he coaxed, 'you were about to say something. What was it?'

She giggled. 'Oh well, you asked for it—men, I suppose. My cousin Dee's always telling me I set impossibly high standards. She says, you want a saint, not a human being. But the way I see it is, if I can't respect a man, why should I devote my life to him?'

'Is that what you intend to do?'

Her eyes sparkled. 'Oh, well, not devote

exactly, but you know what I mean! You have to spend an awful lot of time with someone when you're married to them. Imagine having to spend it with someone you didn't either like or respect? And the two go hand in hand——' She stopped.

His face had adopted a closed look that startled her. She'd never seen anybody wipe the expression off their face so quickly.

'Look, why don't we have a stroll in the gardens while dinner's being prepared?' He stood abruptly. 'There's a view of the island from the upper terrace.'

Puzzled by his sudden change of mood, she rose to her feet too. 'I didn't realise it was visible from here.' She gave him a puzzled glance, but he was already coming round the table, pulling back her chair, and she went on, 'With all the problems of getting there I've hardly given the place itself a thought. I think I half believe it's in some never-never land over the rim of the world.'

'Like the land of lost delight?' he murmured. 'A quaint thought. I like it.' He laughed softly, his eyes warm again as he looked down at her.

For one suspenseful moment Shanna thought he was going to kiss her. They were standing so close to each other that it would have been an easy movement for her to bring that blond head a fraction lower, for her own dark one to tilt . . . but something came between them like a shadow. He frowned, turned and said prosaic-

ally, 'We'd better not be too long. Luisa will go
mad if we're late for her fish soup.'

Shaken by the trifling incident of whether he
really had intended to kiss her or not, she
followed along a narrow path between late
blooming hibiscus. He climbed rapidly ahead to
a further terrace on a level with the roof of the
villa.

When they neared the top he stopped. 'Close
your eyes,' he ordered before allowing her to go
on. 'Let's do this properly.' She shut them and
felt him take her by the arm, guiding her a few
steps higher, and then, after a short pause, she
heard him saying quietly, 'All right. Now open
them.'

He had turned her so that the first thing she
saw as her eyes opened was a sea the colour of
lavender, and after a moment she managed to
pick out a darker shape, lying like a sleeping
animal, deep purple against the lighter shade of
the sea. The sky behind it was pale blue. Star-
filled. Moonless. The beauty of the scene struck
her deeply. There was a profound silence.

'The land of lost delight . . .?' She turned to
him. 'So that's what it looks like.' She felt
stirred by the idea. Then she remembered this
was her inheritance.

'Take care,' he warned. 'You may be
disappointed.' He put both hands in his pockets
and moved away.

Shyly she moved after him. 'Whether I'm
disappointed depends on what happens when I

get there, doesn't it?' She gave a tiny laugh,
anticipating with delight the prospect of what
lay ahead. It gave her face a sudden radiance.

He moved back towards her. 'What do you
expect to happen?' he asked in a voice like
velvet, his eyes drinking in her beauty and
making no secret of the fact. 'Love? The
discovery of your heart's desire?' He gave a
harsh laugh. 'Not on Tago Mago, that's for
sure.'

'Who knows?' she objected, confused by his
bitterness. Then, biting her lip, she added in a
practical tone of voice, 'But I'm only here on a
short visit. I don't expect anything to happen,
so I'm not going to be disappointed, am I?'

'A short visit?' He gave her a soft look and
turned away. 'Anything can happen in a short
visit. Beware!'

'Wait!' She made a step to follow him, didn't
notice there was a drop of some inches and fell
achingly to her knees. He was by her side in a
trice but she was up at once, stepping back out
of his reach, then stumbling so that he caught
her anyway and she found herself swept
strongly into his arms. Her face brushed his
cheek as he pulled her close then, without either
of them seeming to plan it, his lips searched for
her own and they met in a warm and sudden
collision. Long after such a kiss should have
ended it went on, his lips insatiably plundering
and exploring and taking their fill, and to her
astonishment Shanna found herself yielding

wantonly as if she had been waiting for this very thing since the moment they had met.

When he finally lifted his head, she felt a shudder like a shock-wave of loss as the distance increased between them. Before she could bring her reeling senses to order, however, he stepped back, giving her an amused smile. It wiped from her mind any intimation of something more profound implied by the sweetness and power he had just bestowed, and sent her trembling back with a little exclamation of dismay. She stared back at him out of the growing darkness.

'There was no need to do that!' she objected.

'No need,' he agreed. 'No need at all.' He gave her another amused glance as if he was likely to do it again whether there was a need or not. 'What's one kiss, anyway?' he asked harshly.

He started to go back down the steps. Shanna felt furious with him, with herself, with Tago Mago for weaving its spell, and with the whole pointless journey. Why had he kissed her as if it meant something when it so obviously didn't? He had kissed her as she had never been kissed before, in an unbelievably passionate way, yet gently, romantically, as if he cared deeply. But, she remembered, they were strangers and, after tonight, might never meet again.

She pushed past him on the narrow path. 'You're right,' she told him icily, 'let's go down to eat. I'm starving.'

Head high, she marched straight back towards the lower terrace, not caring whether he was following or not. When she reached their table he was still only half-way down, but Luisa came out as if she had been waiting for them and placed two bowls of soup on the table.

Paul eventually took his place on the opposite side. He didn't mention the incident that had sent her scurrying off but carefully broke off a piece of bread, tasting his soup with a thoughtful expression, only looking up when he reached across to pour the wine. There was a glint of something in his eyes she was unable to call amusement. It made her wonder what he really did feel, but then she remembered his warning about being disappointed with the land of lost delight.

'Are you offended?' he asked bluntly, breaking into her thoughts.

She raised her eyes to his, then, seeing the expression on his face, couldn't help shaking her head. 'It was as much my fault as yours, as much Tago Mago's fault.' She smiled ruefully. 'Not that that alters the fact that you're quite hateful. I suppose you go around kissing everybody all the time?'

He laughed. 'Only if they happen to be you,' he said, his eyes lazing over her upturned face. 'You're quite irresistible, Shanna. Full of light and laughter. God knows, I can do with someone like you right now!' For a brief moment his eyes darkened, until the by now familiar spark of amusement returned. 'You're beautiful, you know, with such classic good looks.'

She scowled, unwilling to succumb to overt flattery. She knew she was pretty, her mirror told her that, but she only saw her looks as an accident of nature, something for which she was not responsible. Looks were useful in her job, though people were always trying to encourage her to go into the modelling side which she didn't want. Now it seemed they had other uses, though what real purpose there was in furthering a relationship with a man she would probably never see again she couldn't imagine.

She gave him a haughty glance, then, catching his eyes, couldn't help grinning. 'You're not so bad yourself, actually,' she told him.

He chuckled. 'Now I know we've achieved equality, when a girl can embarrass a man by complimenting him on his looks!'

'Are you embarrassed?' He seemed to fumble for words, and before he could reply she went on, 'I don't see what's wrong with telling you if it's true, though of course you must know!'

'Looks, dear Shanna, as I'm sure you've been told before, are not everything.' He frowned. 'They can be a curse as well as an advantage.' He looked up. 'Not to someone like you, though, I hope. You're refreshingly down-to-earth. It makes a change from these spoiled professional beauties.'

'Well, lucky it's now so dark,' she observed. 'Perhaps we'll both see things differently in the morning!'

He chuckled again. 'Sweet, you really are sweet. Now tell me all about yourself.'

It was late by the time they finished talking. Dinner had been cleared away long ago, and they shared a bottle of the local brandy as a nightcap. She was astonished at the enormous quantity they seemed to have consumed. It had loosened her tongue, though she felt clear-headed, every nerve sensitive to the nuance of his voice in the darkness.

Despite her intentions he had gleaned a lot about her background, about how she had been brought up between boarding-school and the home of an older cousin, and about Dee, yet another cousin, with whom she was now sharing a flat in London.

She didn't tell him about her inheritance. Something stopped her; a feeling, maybe, that it would be seen as an attempt to impress. And she wasn't entirely sure he would believe her. Having seen it now and suddenly realised for the first time that it wasn't just a name on a piece of paper, she could scarcely believe herself that she owned it. Part-owned it.

'I'm sorry,' she stopped in mid-sentence, 'but you haven't told me a thing about yourself. You've let me rabbit on all evening. It must be really boring for you!'

'Not at all. I could sit and listen to you for ever.' He took her hand in his. 'You're like a breath of spring, Shanna. Just what the doctor ordered!' Lines of pain surrounded his mouth, only noticeable when his eyes became sombre. She let her hand lie there in his, enjoying the delicious feelings it seemed to transmit.

'I suppose after tonight,' she began, 'we won't meet——' then she broke off. It seemed unbearable to think they wouldn't meet again, but having nearly blurted out the obvious it sounded as if she were forcing the issue.

But he half turned, peering at her through the darkness, his eyes two dark hollows. 'We shall meet again. I hope it won't be a disappointment . . .' He too failed to finish what he had been going to say, instead adding abruptly, 'How about inspecting your embarkation point?'

'A walk to the cove? Lovely! Perhaps we'll get a moonlight swim, too!' His abrupt change of subject puzzled her. He was an enigma, but one she wanted to understand.

He linked his arm in hers and they moved off into the darkness, only the sound of their footsteps audible on the road outside the gate. Then they left the road and went by a path leading directly to the beach. The air was aromatic with the scent of wild thyme and other sweet herbs. As they approached the sea a warm breeze blew inland with a promise in it of fair days.

Shanna had expected the cove to be tiny and

it was, but as they tramped softly through the sand towards the water-line she saw it open out into an endless expanse, its limits indistinct in the darkness but appearing to stretch on endlessly into the purple night.

It brought a sudden sense of freedom, and she ran on ahead, some wild urge making her turn cartwheels in the soft sand. They were something she had always been good at and she laughed aloud with the sheer joy of living.

When Paul caught up with her she said, 'It's wonderful! Cala Longa! And I called it a dot on the map! How insulting. I hope it'll forgive me!' She danced down to the water's edge again, her sandals long since discarded as she ran into the waves.

Paul watched her in astonishment for a moment, then, kicking off his black espadrilles, ran down to join her. Shanna jumped over the tops of the breakers, her skirt held high in one hand, spirits raised by the sound of the surf rolling in. When she turned her heart seemed to do a cartwheel too. Paul looked so handsome, so stern, somehow, standing there in the night. Then he caught her glance and threw back his head and began to laugh.

'You're crazy, Shanna Douglas! Do you know that?' The dazzle of surf seemed to surround him like an aura, and phosphorescence made the scene unreal. It was a night of magic.

'It's warm enough for a swim!' she called,

splashing through the water towards him. She went right up to him before she saw the changed expression on his face. It pulled her up short. His smile had saddened and he was watching her with a strange yearning in his eyes, like someone looking in at something they could never have.

Confused, she let her laughter die away. 'Have I done something wrong?' she asked hurriedly, coming to a stop.

'Not wrong, no!' he muttered, turning away. He began to walk rapidly through the water parallel to the beach and she caught up with him, tramping silently by his side until he turned and stared out to sea. Following his glance, she saw that he was staring out at the dark bulk of Tago Mago, a shuttered look on his face that set her thoughts racing. Not daring to risk another question, she stood beside him without speaking.

'So,' he said at last, 'that's where you'll be tomorrow night?' He turned and glanced down at her, then quickly away again, gazing off into the distance. 'Where do you intend to put up?' he asked.

'In the villa, of course.'

With a look of something like resignation he reached out, taking her by both hands and drawing her close so he could look straight into her eyes. In the darkness his own gleamed like polished stone, drained of colour, but full of depth and meaning beneath the deeply arched brows.

Shanna knew he would kiss her, knew she would be unable to resist if he wanted her, and it made her draw in her breath as if preparing for flight.

Then she felt herself being hauled slowly in towards the irresistible aura of his physical perfection, the heat of his desire pulsing towards her like a blatant emanation of his will.

He wanted her. She was young enough to be shocked by the raw strength of his need. There was shock in the force of such a blatant desire, its primitive urgency crying out to something in her too, something unawakened before this moment.

'You beautiful creature, I do so want you,' he groaned, dragging her up against him and crushing his mouth down on hers. She was helpless beneath his touch, feeling herself go under, unresisting, swept by a tide of emotion wholly new, and like an *ingénue* she felt an avid desire to learn all the unexperienced nuances of his touch, to discover in lessons of love things she had never imagined. The sea cradled them in a swooning lullaby, night locked them in its private heaven, and she felt his body slide over hers, bringing her down beneath him at the water's edge. They rolled over and over, half in and half out of the salt spray, sand yielding to the pressure of their bodies and the colder liquid of the ocean caressing them in its ceaseless lapping and leaving.

Paul ran his hands equally down both sides

of her body, kneading her melting limbs to the shape of his desire, his voice, when he raised his head to speak, muffled with wanting.

'Don't make me desire you, Shanna. It's not going to work! Stop me, darling, unless you really want me,' he mumbled against the side of her cheek.

Her head fluttered from side to side as if to free herself from the constraint of saying what she knew she must, but the words remained locked in her throat.

'Stop me,' he urged, 'say it. Stop me. Think of tomorrow. Regrets, regrets, Shanna. Stop me, angel.'

'Yes,' she breathed, not knowing whether it was a yes of assent to the imperative of their bodies' need or a yes in agreement with the words of restraint he urged. 'Yes, Paul . . . yes,' she said as her body belied her intentions, answering his need with her own. 'I can't . . . I need you . . . I can't . . .'

What it was she couldn't admit was lost in the roar of the surf as a series of waves rolled them over. The cold water came between, separating them for a moment, long enough for Paul to drag himself up, pulling her into the crook of his arms, caressing her, but carefully holding her, calming and controlling his desire and hers with an effort of will, tightening his grasp as she undulated against him in open need.

'No, love,' he murmured, voice hoarse with thwarted desire, 'tomorrow you would hate me and I couldn't take that. And, listen, I don't want you to get hurt.' He held her still. 'It's the magic, that's all. It's the magic of Tago Mago . . . Please, my sweet, no, still now, gently.' He stroked her hair, tried not to kiss her, but felt his lips follow her hairline in a tantalising spiral that made her drag his head down hard so that his lips touched hers, escaping and returning again and again.

With an effort he brought them both at last to their feet. Unable to tear themselves apart for more than a moment, they began to walk slowly back up the deserted beach towards the villa. It was after midnight. The warm night air dried their clothes and by the time they reached the terrace Shanna felt the fine silk of her skirt dry against her legs, only her hair, twisted in corkscrew curls by the surf, pressing damply around her shoulders.

She felt herself tremble to imagine what had been so near, tremble with loss and a yearning for what might have been, but tremble with gratitude too for the strength that had staved off an even greater future loss.

The stark fact was that the moment was approaching when he would turn and say goodnight, goodbye, and she was scarcely aware of the soft words whispered in her ear, the meaning of which lit a spark of hope when once she heeded them.

'And that's a promise,' he murmured as he bent to caress her cheek. 'But I doubt whether you'll thank me for keeping it.'

'We shall meet again?' she repeated in bewilderment. 'A promise?' Her heart fluttered with hope, despite his strange warning.

'We'll meet again, my love. Trust me. Trust in me, whatever happens.'

'Why ever should I not?' she breathed, running her fingers through his spiky blond hair and helplessly bringing his head down again so that his lips could meet her own.

He walked with her to the door of the villa, pushing her gently inside. 'Moonlight bathing . . .' He gave a gentle chuckle. 'It's a million years since I did anything like that. Here's to the next time!' Bending over her hands, he kissed the backs then stepped away. 'Go now. Sleep. Dream. Trust me.'

Without another word he swivelled and began to walk rapidly away down the drive. She watched the pale starlit figure dwindle between the trees until it was a grey shadow among other shadows, indistinguishable from the night.

She wondered where he was going to stay and if they would really meet again. Something extraordinary seemed to have happened to her, and she had never been on such intimate terms with anyone ever before. The night had been an endless exploration, as if they had taken up where they had left off in some other life.

CHAPTER THREE

AS SHE had been bidden, Shanna arrived on the beach with her black leather travel-bag at nine o'clock the next morning. A sleepless night in which she had been taunted by the remembered touch of an enigmatic stranger had left her feeling drained, but to a casual observer she looked merely pale, with an intriguing, fragile beauty ill-disguised by scrubbed blue jeans and the clumpy trainers substituted for yesterday's sandals.

She wondered again where Paul had walked off to in the night, and whether he would be waiting for her this morning at the beach, but the figure already sitting in a boat moored at the end of a rough stone jetty was not him and she stifled her disappointment under a cheerful smile.

When she reached the end of the jetty she eyed the launch with misgivings. Little more than a rowing-boat with a small outboard, it looked too fragile to negotiate the strong currents of the channel separating the two islands.

Wondering again if she should have heeded everyone's advice and simply sold her share in the island, she stepped down into the fragile shell, pushing her bag underneath one of the seats and hoping it would stand up to the effects of sea-water.

The occupant of the boat, an old fisherman with a face like tanned leather, nodded a greeting, and, either because he knew she wouldn't understand or because he was naturally taciturn, proceeded to untie the painter without further preamble.

Soon they were rocking over the waves, a fresh breeze bringing a flush of delicate colour to Shanna's cheeks. Her hair was quickly knotted by the wind and she wished she had a headscarf. Unsure what lay ahead, she wanted to look her best, but after dabbing ineffectually at her flying locks she soon gave it up as a bad job and let the wind do what it would.

As they approached the island the boat began to plunge and dip more alarmingly through the rip-tide that lay like a barrier in mid-channel. The old man sat calmly at the helm, ignoring the sudden splash of water hitting the bows and scattering icy drops into the boat, but Shanna soon felt wet and shivery and she scanned the approaching coastline for a sign of journey's end with impatience. There seemed to be nothing ahead except jagged cliffs and a tiny yellow strand beneath a jutting rock. No wonder there isn't a regular ferry service, she thought. It isn't the sort of place to which anybody but a real world-hater would want to

come. Then she remembered Great-Aunt Vi.
Certainly no world-hater, she had sought the
seclusion of Tago Mago only after she married
her fourth husband, who was with her to the
end. This much she had managed to glean from
Mr Metcalf. He had also told her that her great-
aunt made frequent and protracted visits to
various parts of the world even just before her
final illness. Much of her time, in fact, was
spent at one or other of her houses in Florida or
Scotland.

She began to shiver now as she looked
around, partly with cold, but mainly with fear
at the sight of the massive red cliffs which as
they approached seemed to loom with a definite
sense of foreboding, making their boat seem
tiny, like a fragile leaf on the waves. It would be
a dour place in the depths of winter.

With a display of unexpected skill the skipper
guided the boat between two partly submerged
rocks, and then suddenly there was a stretch of
sheltered water with a real jetty ahead, and they
were skimming across the unrippled waters
within the harbour. The old man brought the
boat up to the wall, throwing an old rope
around the lower rung of a metal ladder set in
the slabs. Then, courteously guiding Shanna up
the ladder, he handed her bag up after her and
finally, with a hand raised in farewell, turned
the bows towards the harbour entrance again. It
was all done so quickly that soon all that was left
was the lapping of the water as the wake washed

against the smooth stones below where she stood.

Alone, Shanna desperately wished for Paul to be beside her. The folly of coming all this way and being unable to talk to anyone struck her as absurd now. Still, what's done is done, she chided herself, preparing for an uphill climb to the top of the cliff. Wondering if anyone would be coming down to meet her, for someone must have noticed her arrival, she trudged gamely on, expecting at any moment to be hailed. But she reached the top with only the cry of sea-birds for company.

She stopped, panting a little, and gazed around. So this was it, this was her inheritance!

The island was small enough to see right across to the other side, but its sharp crags and sudden gulfs were enough to keep any secrets hidden. A single track wound away towards a small group of wind-buffeted trees, and beyond that was a wall with a hint of roofs beyond. There was an air of orderliness, a neatness in the clipped grass and white-painted walls, and in the more sheltered dips flowers bloomed in a profusion of late blossoms.

As she approached she couldn't help feeling a kindling of the excitement she had first felt when she'd learned she was the owner of an island. Part-owner, she corrected herself once again. If only Richard Mather was here to share this fleeting moment, she thought, for soon this unexpected pride of ownership would be only a memory.

Everything was quiet as she approached an
open wrought-iron gate. Beyond it was an
enclosed courtyard, paved lavishly in traditional
Spanish tiles, and within, visible through a line
of palms, the bright turquoise of a swimming
pool. A couple of loungers were placed
haphazardly half in and half out of the sun.
Shanna gasped at the unexpected luxury of the
scene, having already convinced herself that so
inaccessible a place must be primitive in every
sense.

Now, coming closer, she saw that it was what
Dee would have called a haven for the idle rich.
Drinks on a painted trolley stood on the terrace
steps, and from somewhere inside she could
hear the sound of dance music from a powerful
stereo. Sheltered as it was in a hollow of the
island, the courtyard was surrounded by
profusely growing palms, and over the shallow
pitch of the red roof she saw the tops of others
like clipped flowers, stark and glossy.

Wondering how to make her arrival known,
she walked towards the edge of the pool, gazing
across it towards the open french doors in the
hope of catching sight of someone. Then there
was a sound above her head.

'I don't believe it!' exclaimed a voice from
inside the villa. A man's face appeared at a first-
floor window. 'You can't be the new owner?
Never!' A hearty laugh followed and then the
sound of sandalled feet flapped across a marble

floor. The plump figure of a man in a bright Bermuda shirt and shorts, and obviously the owner of one of the half-filled glasses on the trolley beside the loungers, came hurrying down steps that ran up the outside of the villa to the first-floor balcony.

He came swiftly towards her, hands out-stretched in greeting. 'Metcalf said you were young, but honestly, you're nothing but a babe in arms.' He shook her hand vigorously before she could say anything, then stepped back and gave her a close look.

'Of course you're not going to hang on to the old place, are you? It's like a sponge, dearie, but it's money not water the place absorbs. Don't be taken in by the air of decadent luxury——' he waved a pudgy hand '—it all costs, dearie, it all costs. Luckily Vi had the wherewithal and so, I gather——' he glanced hurriedly from side to side '—does the new man.'

'The who?' asked Shanna stepping forward as if to receive a secret confidence.

'The Mr Moneybags who wants to buy us out. Well, now, what can I get you? Gin and tonic, Martini and lemon, Bacardi and soda? Or would you prefer our own label——' Again he glanced from side to side.

'No, really, it's a little early——' Shanna protested, taken aback by all the things this stranger had told her even before she had managed to draw breath.

'Ah! I can see you're not used to island life, time standing still, all that. At least, it does on Tago Mago. The thing to do is go with it. Go with it, dearie.' He raised his glass in a salute.

'I didn't know anyone was actually living here,' she remarked, feeling hopelessly out of her depth. 'Mr Metcalf was fairly vague. To tell you the truth I don't think he knew very much, but he gave me to understand there was a housekeeper and some other staff employed by my Aunt Vi who were all working out their notice——' She stopped abruptly, wondering if she had been tactless, but her companion smiled pleasantly.

'Quite right, too!' As if to scotch any idea she might be the smallest bit wrong, he shook his head vigorously. 'All staff. All tried and trusted employees. Nobody else here. Not a soul. Island empty. Don't bother your head about that. No permission to build, you see.' Then he gave her a sideways glance. 'You're the only other one here apart from staff.'

'What about Richard Mather? I gather the sale can't go ahead without his signature too. Have they managed to contact him?' she asked.

The man shook his head. 'They will. Don't worry. You ignore him. No need to bother about him at all.'

Shanna frowned. 'Well, it's certainly difficult enough to get here,' she went on feelingly. 'I hope he manages all right!'

The fat man merely gave an odd smile and turned to refill his drink from the trolley beside the lounger. When he turned back he said, 'My name's Arthur. I was your aunt's general factotum. Henry isn't here. He had to go away on business.'

'Henry?'

'Vi's number four.'

'Four?'

'Husband, dearie.' He gave her a puzzled frown.

Feeling like a fool, Shanna nodded. Just then they were interrupted by a woman's voice from within the villa. A figure came into view in one of the doorways. Evidently a housekeeper from the severe grey bun and the apron she wore over a pair of slacks and a pale pink sweater, she came out on to the terrace. 'Leave the poor girl alone, Arthur. She's probably feeling sea-sick,' she called in greeting.

'No, I'm not——' protested Shanna. I'm just a little confused, she thought to herself, glancing from one to the other.

'A nice cup of English tea will soon solve that,' said the housekeeper as she came towards her. 'Come into the kitchen, and Arthur,' she turned to the fat man, 'go and warn Jorge about the landing. He'll be here soon.'

More puzzled than ever by the housekeeper's cryptic words, Shanna obediently followed her inside.

It was equally sumptuous, with polished

wooden floors scattered with bright designer
rugs, paintings covering the walls with warm
and subtle colourings and gold gleaming in little
shafts from the furniture and ornaments. There
was a kind of atrium in the middle of the villa
and the housekeeper led Shanna briskly across it
and into a cluttered kitchen. 'Cook won't mind
if we help ourselves,' she observed, preparing
tea in a china pot. 'I'm Katerina, your great-
aunt's housekeeper,' she explained. 'How long
do you want to stay? Long enough to be glad
you've had an offer on the place, I suppose?'

'I—I don't know. But, yes,' she admitted
slowly after a moment's thought, 'I suppose I
shall sell. But it's also up to Richard Mather
too. It's not just my decision.'

'He won't want the trouble of a place like
this.' She sniffed. 'When Vi told us what she
was going to do it was a bit of shock. I think she
harboured a lot of romantic ideas. I don't know
what you feel about it?'

Shanna looked puzzled. 'How do you mean?
I don't think I understand.'

'She was always a bit of match-maker, your
great-aunt. Best heart in the world. But
romantic. Unconventional. She seems to have
imagined that you and Richard might get
together. As business partners, well, who knows
what it might lead to? she said. Personally I
think she might have consulted you both. From
what I hear Richard is the same as when he was
a lad. I can't imagine him settling down in a

place like this. And for all Vi knew he could have had a little wife tucked away in Asia somewhere. He's been out there for years now.'

'How old is this Richard Mather?' asked Shanna cautiously.

'Older than you. The perfect age for a husband, said Vi, and she should know!'

'What, about thirty?'

'Early thirties, yes.'

'Is he nice?' Her eyes sparkled mischievously.

'I haven't seen him since he was a boy. He used to come out in the holidays sometimes. Always up to mischief. Yes,' she paused, 'I should think a girl like you might go for that type. More fool you if you do. He always had a real wanderlust. You'd have to be pretty self-sufficient to make a go of family life with a man like Richard!' Though it was a criticism, she was smiling as she spoke, and Shanna guessed she had a soft spot for this Richard Mather.

'What does he do?' she asked. 'For a living, I mean?'

'Same as Vi. Travel writing. Knocking about in every unlikely godforsaken bit of a country he can find. Roughing it. That's what he does for a living. Roughs it.'

'He sounds quite swashbuckling,' she mused, drawing a pattern with her fingertip on the kitchen worktop.

'Yes, you would say that. You'll be a romantic like your great-aunt, no doubt. Well,

all I can say is, lass, watch your step. He's the
love 'em   and leave 'em type, I wouldn't
wonder. Not that it's my place to have an
opinion.' She patted Shanna on the arm.
'You're a pretty little lass. I can't quite think of
you as the landlady!'

'Good, because I don't feel like one!' She got
up. 'What will you do when the place is sold,
Katerina?'

The older woman became serious. 'Me and
Arthur, you mean? Well, we always thought of
retiring somewhere like this. But who knows,
we're not in line for our pension yet. And this
one who's putting in a bid for the place, maybe
he'll keep us on?'

'Oh, I do hope so. If he's not going to, maybe
Richard and I should try to keep things going?'

Katerina shook her head. 'It's a kind
thought, but I don't think you understand all
the problems with a place like this. Take my
advice, my dear: sell up. Don't bother about us.
For all we know, the man who's offering so
much for it will keep us on. And why not?
We're a good team and we can run this place
with our hands tied behind our backs. What's
more, it's nearly impossible to keep staff
in a place like this. Who wants to live on a
remote lump of rock cut off from the rest of the
world?'

Shanna felt like pointing out that Katerina
and Arthur obviously did, but she felt it
wouldn't be polite. She couldn't help feeling

intrigued by the housekeeper's description of
Richard Mather, and she wondered if he would
show up before she left. The trouble was, she
had only intended to stay for a day or two.

As if to confirm this, Katerina looked down at
Shanna's one piece of luggage. 'Not brought
much with you. Is that all of it?'

When Shanna nodded she gave a slight smile.
'Come along, then. I'll show you the guest-
room.'

Soon Shanna was alone again. Thoughts of
Paul came flooding back as she sank down on to
the bed and closed her eyes. What had he
meant by asking her to trust him? Why had he
said they would meet again? And why was
she so intrigued by the idea of Richard Mather?
As a travel writer did he perhaps have an alias?
Like 'Paul Elliot', for instance?

She kicked off her trainers and wondered
whether to get changed into something prettier.
Perhaps when she returned to the main island,
to Cala Longa or Santa Eulalia, she would
bump into Paul again.

The thought of doing in reverse the journey
she had just completed filled her with weariness.
Only Paul's presence would make it bearable.

With a start she opened her eyes. She must have
dozed off for a moment. The roar of an engine
filled her ears. It was directly overhead.
Confused for a moment, she suddenly realised
what it was. Slipping off the bed, she ran to

the window and looked out. A scarlet helicopter
was passing over. If she craned her neck she
could just make out its gigantic, somehow
threatening shape as it lumbered over the
island. Then she had a moment's panic as it
seemed about to crash on to the cliffs on the
other side before she realised it was trying to
make a landing. The housekeeper's instructions
to Arthur came back. Now it made sense—there
must be a pad somewhere, she registered. Some
lucky devil knows how to get on and off without having to go through the rigmarole of taxis
and outboard motor-boats, she thought.

She watched for a moment or two, expecting
to see the passengers walking over the hill
towards the villa, but the helicopter was out of
sight and no one appeared in view. Deciding to
take a closer look and eager to see the rest of her
island, she slipped her shoes back on and went
downstairs. There was no one around, the
loungers were empty, and the pool lay like a
splinter of lapis lazuli now the sun had shifted.

Pausing for only a second at the gate, she
turned inland, intending to cut right across the
island to the far side. There was no path, but
it would surely be no more than a fifteen-minute
walk.

She was wrong. After a good twenty minutes
she was still labouring up the side of a steep hill.
It was so steep in parts that she had to go on
hands and knees. Regretting her hasty decision
to explore without first talking to either Arthur

or Katerina, she scrambled the last few yards then paused breathlessly at the top. There was a ravine below, with a small wooden footbridge leading to the other side. Determined now to go on—after all, her time was her own and the place did partly belong to her—she set off, slipping and sliding down the other side until she reached some stone steps leading on to the bridge. She was just about to put out a hand to grasp the wooden rail when a voice overhead gave a shout.

'Shanna!'

She tilted her head, squinting against the sun, and could just make out a dark shape outlined on the clifftop on the other side.

'I wouldn't if I were you!' came the warning. It was a voice she recognised, sending shivers of surprise and pleasure racing through her veins.

'Paul! I can't believe it!' She still couldn't see him, but the voice was unmistakable. The silhouette disappeared and she saw the familiar figure in the white clothes, hair bright against the darker rock, come scrambling down the cliff towards her.

'Do you think it looks safe?' he asked when he reached the other side of the footbridge. 'I wouldn't risk it!' There was only a yard or two separating them, but below, far below, were savage rocks in a tumble of lethal spikes.

'I still can't believe this!' exclaimed Shanna, not trying to disguise her pleasure. 'How did you get here? Was it you in the helicopter?

Oh, Paul, why on earth didn't you tell me you were coming over?'

'I told you we would meet again.' He didn't make any move to cross the bridge and Shanna took a step forward, intending to join him.

'No, don't.' He glanced back up the cliff. 'Look, Shanna—don't come any further. I've got to go now.'

'But I——'

'Don't argue.' His face looked harsh, stern lines etched in it, the look of cold decision on it she had noticed with misgiving at their earlier meeting.

'If you say so——' she agreed, reluctantly. 'But aren't you coming over here? Can't we talk properly?'

Once again he glanced up the cliff-face in the direction from which he had appeared. 'There isn't time. I'll contact you later. Now, go back to the Villa Mimosa and don't come this way again.' He started to turn.

Shanna couldn't bear to see him leave. 'Please, Paul,' she called as he began to climb back up the cliff. 'Don't go.'

'Do as I say. Now go back.' He gave her a look that stopped her in her tracks. Observing her expression, he paused, looking down at her with a softening in the harsh features, and said, 'Don't worry. You'll see me soon enough!' With that he completed the rest of the climb and disappeared over the top of the ridge.

Puzzled, Shanna made her way back the

way she had come. Why shouldn't she cross the bridge? And what on earth was Paul doing here, acting like a fugitive, yet so clearly used to having people obey him without question?

She wended her way back, in no hurry to return, but unsure which direction to take now that she was within sight of the villa and the obvious route to the other side of the island had been closed to her.

Arthur was lounging by the pool when she re-entered the courtyard.

'Been for walkies, dearie?' he called, giving her a shrewd glance that took in the dust-stained trainers. 'You want to be careful, it's not the safest of islands. Too many crumbly cliffs. Personally, I never leave the villa. It's safer that way.'

She sat down on the seat he pushed forward. 'Do you go over to the mainland very often?' she asked, feeling trapped.

'Only when I get island phobia,' he replied, 'and that only happens once in a blue moon. I like it here. But it's no good for somebody with all their life ahead of them. You'd hate it in winter. There's not even a boat to get you off then.'

'What about a helicopter?' she asked.

'Oh, so you heard it, did you?' He hesitated, as if making up his mind what to say next. 'It was probably just a visitor.' He looked at her carefully. 'Maybe it's the man who's going to buy?'

'If I sell. If Richard and I decide to sell,' she corrected.

'He will. Mather. Needs the money, I hear. It's up to you. You're not serious about not selling, are you?' His pale eyes in the pudgy face suddenly looked worried, narrowing, almost losing themselves in the folds of loose flesh.

'I think I might be allowed to make up my own mind, don't you?' Feeling pressured and getting rather tired of being told what to do, she got up and made her way inside.

Later Shanna had gone back to find Arthur to apologise for walking off and they had had a nice chat, he mentioning in passing a small private cove where she could swim. Somehow pleased to be away from the villa, knowing that to some extent she had the future of its occupants in her hands, she had escaped with a towel and swimsuit in the direction he had described. She had believed she would be alone and had stretched out, nearly naked on the fine white sand. She must have dropped off to sleep, for the next thing she knew a hand was brushing her forehead, pushing the dark hair gently back from her face. Her eyes snapped open, sending her bolt upright.

A soft laugh made her turn her head. Paul was crouching beside her in the sand, all trace of his former coldness gone as he laughed down at her.

'You did look sweet. I've been watching you for ages.' He leaned forward and took her in his arms. 'Sorry about all the cloak and dagger stuff. There's a very good reason.'

She waited for him to explain, but he said simply, 'Trust me, Shanna, will you?'

'Of course I trust you!' she exclaimed. 'Why shouldn't I?'

But when he still didn't make her any the wiser she simply relaxed in his arms, feeling safe, protected by his warmth, despite the strangeness of his words. Automatically her head tilted, and she shivered as his lips came down over hers. But he pulled away and murmured, 'I can't stay long. I just wanted to hold you and try to explain a little bit about the situation I find myself in.'

'It's all right.' She gave him a shy look. 'I had a bit of a chat with Katerina at the villa and something she said made me start thinking.' She leaned her face against his shoulder. 'I think I've guessed who you are. It's all right. Don't worry. I understand.'

There was a pause. Paul rose hurriedly to his feet. 'Shanna, what do you think now you've seen the island? You're not seriously considering keeping it on, are you?'

'Don't you want to?' Convinced he must be Richard Mather and for some reason didn't want his presence at the villa to be known just yet, she knelt at his feet, looking up at him in surprise. 'I had a wild thought you'd want to keep it. But I guess it is impracticable without pots of loot.'

He looked confused. 'Go home. It's really not worth all the hassle.'

'I'm sick of people telling me to go home! What if I like it here? What if I want to keep it on?'

'It's not just your decision.'

'I know, I know, but do you mean you wouldn't keep it—at any price?' she demanded. 'If you do, then I guess that's the end of all my hopes too. I mean—I'm just beginning to think seriously about it. I like it here. It could be developed or something.' She looked around in confusion. 'As long as we kept within governmental guidelines,' she added as an afterthought.

'It's not worth the trouble, believe me. Why not just take the money and run?'

'Is that what you want to do?'

When he didn't answer she rose to her feet. 'I suppose you're right. I could never buy you out.' She shrugged. 'Pity. For a couple of hours at least I've been enjoying this place. I started to like the idea of owning an island, after all.' She sighed. 'But I guess it's just a romantic dream. Katerina said Great-Aunt Vi was a romantic——' She stopped, blushing, remembering the rest of what she had said. 'You're right,' she mumbled, going back to her original tack. 'Everybody's right. They all agree. It would be stupid to refuse such a good offer.

This business consortium, whoever they are, will get what they want. Though why they should want it I've no idea.'

'Probably heard that somebody else is after it and want a piece of the action,' he said sharply. Then he stepped forward and took her in his arms. 'I'm truly sorry.' He brushed his lips across her forehead. 'I suppose that means you can leave first thing in the morning? There's nothing much to keep you here. I'll fix the boat to come out if you like.'

She gave him a puzzled look. 'You, Arthur, Katerina—you all seem very glad to see the back of me. And this chap who arrived by helicopter, no doubt he'd be keen to see me go too.' She sighed and pulled a little face. 'I've never felt *persona non grata* before. But who am I to stay when I'm not wanted?'

She felt hurt that Paul seemed so relieved she was leaving. The touch of his arms brought an uncontrollable thrill to her senses, and it hurt to think he didn't feel the same. Yet, when their lips met, how could it be such magic for her and not for him? She tilted her head back so she could read the expression on his face, desperate for the smallest sign of regret that they were soon to part.

He seemed to be eyeing her with an alert watchfulness, and she felt a wave of disappointment sweeping over her. She knew that for her it was more than mere physical attraction, though she would have been the

first to admit that it was his animal masculine
power that first started to weave some kind of
spell over her. But it was the losing of this
something more she felt that pained her like the
wrenching of a knife in the stomach.

'Oh, Paul—whoever . . .' She fingered the
edge of his jacket collar, not sure how to go
on. Plunging on before she lost the feeling of
recklessness that was sweeping her along, she
murmured, 'I can't bear the thought of never
seeing you again . . . I think . . . I think I really
feel something for you. Something a little bit
frightening. Could it be love?' She bit her lip.
'There, I've said it now.' Abruptly slipping
away from him, she turned and began to run
along the beach, covered in waves of embarrass-
ment.

'Shanna! Where are you going?'

Not trusting herself to answer, she ran down
to the water's edge and began to swim blindly
out to sea. 'Oh hell, hell, hell,' she ground
out as her own salt tears joined the salt water
of the sea. 'I'm swimming in tears,' she
muttered angrily over and over, 'I can't feel like
this over someone I scarcely know. Yet I feel as
if I've known him all my life. Oh, Paul, Paul . . .'
A large wave washed right over her head and
she turned on to her back, kicking out her legs
to return to shore.

Suddenly Paul appeared beside her, swimming strongly. She was glad her tears had been
washed away, and when he took hold of her

by the shoulders, bringing their faces close, she
could see the regret on his face, together with
that enigmatic something else she had seen
before.

She tried to swim away to conceal the
hammering of her heart, but without speaking
he took her in his arms, forcing her to tread
water; then his lips searched for hers and they
undulated among the waves like two creatures
of the sea restored to their rightful element.

Shanna felt her resistance dissolve as his
limbs touched and left and touched again along
the whole drifting length of her body, and they
both slid over and around each other, flowing
like liquid through crystals of light. Paul
released her then took her up again, running
his fingers sensually through the tendrils of
dark hair flowing around her shoulders in the
clear water. Below them sand and coral and the
undulations of sea plants claimed them as
inhabitants of a new world.

When he did speak, the strange shuttered
look came down over his face, but his words
brought a streak of happiness arrowing through
her. Against the side of her face he whispered,
'The feeling is reciprocated. Surely you can tell?
Just remember that, will you? And trust me.'
And despite the expression on his face her heart
told her to trust him, come what may.

'When are you going to explain what's going
on, Paul?' she asked later as they walked back
laced in each other's arms to where they had

left their things.

'I will tell you, I promise. But don't ask me when.'

'So there really is something going on?'

'I guess.' He kicked a pebble along the sand, slowly releasing her. Then he swivelled her round to face him, eyes closed as he brought his lips slowly down to her own. The kiss was long and deep. There was something final about it that made Shanna look up in alarm when he finally released her.

He reached out and let one finger course slowly down the side of her face. 'Be ready to leave first thing in the morning. I'll contact you on the other side,' he said tersely. 'Believe it.'

He must know that's the biggest incentive to leave he could offer, she thought as she watched him walk away along the beach. The other side. I shall see my love on the other side.

Looking out to the huge hump of the main island across the channel, she recalled his words as they had stood looking across at Tago Mago itself the previous night. 'The land of lost delight,' Paul had murmured. Now she was confused. She had thought this was supposed to be that land. But she was being persuaded to leave it by the very man who could make of it a dream come true.

CHAPTER FOUR

WONDERING why Paul hadn't told her from the beginning that he was visiting Tago Mago so that they could then have pooled resources, Shanna pondered events as she changed into her one good dress before dinner. She guessed it must have been as much a shock to Paul, or Richard as he really was, to discover that they were the co-owners of the island.

But why should he be visiting in secret? Was he hoping to avoid being pressurised to sell as she had been until he had a chance to make up his mind properly? Yet he seemed as keen as anybody to get rid of the place.

Frowning, she slicked gloss over her lips, gave her eyelids a dusting of soft colour, and, feeling presentable in her plain black shift, let herself out of her room and made her way down the outer staircase to the terrace. It was wonderful that it was still warm enough to dine outside.

Not expecting anything special, she was surprised to find the table set with tall candlesticks and proper silver. No picnic spread this, she thought, examining with pleasure the way the candlelight glittered off the crystal

goblets, scattering tiny rainbows of colour over
the pale lace cloth.

Cook could be seen in the kitchen through an
open window looking on to the terrace. Shanna
wondered if she would join them for dinner, for
the table was set for four.

As she looked round Arthur appeared silently
in one of the doorways on the other side of the
pool. He didn't appear to see her, but walked
outside with a thoughtful expression, skirting
the pool without looking at it and pausing for
a moment on the far side. It soon became clear
he was waiting for someone, for he glanced at
his watch a couple of times and then, apparently
catching sight of a figure coming in through
the gate, hurried forward with a muffled word
of greeting. Then Shanna gasped. The man
who was coming openly towards the terrace was
no stranger.

It was Paul, as handsome and casually
elegant as ever in a white dinner-jacket, open-
neck silk shirt and pale cream trousers. He
seemed remarkably at ease and it looked
obvious from where Shanna was watching that
he had been here before.

Yet when Arthur noticed her standing beside
the table he hurried back round the pool
towards her, beckoning Paul forward as if to
introduce them both.

Before he could say anything though, Shanna
herself stepped forward, holding out her hand,
fully expecting Arthur to introduce her with the

words, 'This is Richard Mather.'

Instead, Paul took her hand in his and said quickly, 'Yes, we have already met. Shanna——' He bent and dropped a playful kiss on to the back of her hand.

Shanna gulped and, in a dream, found herself holding on to it as if to let it go would be to find herself sinking deeper into fantasy.

Conscious of Arthur's eyes on them both, she turned away as if to admire the table arrangement and, with Arthur's non-stop chatter in her ears, tried to ignore the wild racing of her pulses at Paul's unexpected appearance. When Katerina came out a few moments later and Arthur bustled about supplying them with drinks she allowed herself to join in the conversation, keeping up a superficial chatter that totally concealed how confused she really felt.

She found Katerina giving her a knowing wink as she served the main course, and it was obvious she found the juxtaposition of Paul and herself at the table a source of romantic speculation.

'Why didn't you tell me he was going to show up?' asked Shanna under her breath as she helped clear the table.

'I'd no idea you'd met.'

'But he told me he was called Paul Elliot.'

'Isn't he?' Katerina looked mystified.

'That's one of the names he goes under,' retorted Shanna, smiling to soften the impact of her bewilderment.

Katerina in her turn shot a puzzled look in Shanna's direction, but the baked Alaska was ready to come out of the oven and all her attention was concentrated on that, and by the time they were both sitting at the table again the issue seemed to have taken second place. Paul and Arthur were deep in conversation about the vexing problem of maintaining a reliable electricity supply to the island.

'We have our own generator, but it's fairly unreliable,' Arthur told Shanna. 'But don't run away with the idea I'm trying to put you off——' he laughed, gauging her reaction.

'It's all right,' she told him. 'I've been thoroughly put off the idea of hanging on. I realise there's more to it than I first thought, and frankly I would never be able to raise enough money to run the place properly. Electricity is something that hadn't even crossed my mind. Besides, Paul here has really put me off. He wouldn't want the responsibility either.'

Arthur and Katerina looked first at each other and then at Paul. There was an odd hiatus in the conversation before Paul broke smoothly in with some comment about Katerina's cooking, and the moment of awkwardness vanished. Shanna couldn't help wondering what she had said to provoke that swift exchange of glances.

Dinner passed pleasantly with talk of this and

that, and it was heaven as far as Shanna was
concerned to be sitting opposite Paul. He was so
handsome, so cool, so witty, and she found
herself falling ever deeper under his spell.

Only when conversation turned to Shanna's
early departure on the next day did she sit
up.

'I'm not sure I want to go back so soon,' she
said. 'In fact, if it's all right with you, Katerina,
I'd like to stay one day more. I hope I won't be
encroaching on your hospitality?'

'Not at all, my dear,' Katerina was quick to
reassure her.

'I feel I've scarcely given Great-Aunt Vi a
thought, when in reality I came to, you know,
sort of pay my respects to her. It seemed wrong
just to pocket the money from her gift to me
without trying to discover what it was she loved
about the place——'

'And why she thought it would be a suitable
bequest?' Katerina smiled.

Shanna's glance slid to Paul. She really
hoped Katerina wouldn't mention the nature of
their conversation earlier in the day, in view of
the way she'd already laid her cards on the table
over her feelings for Paul! He would start to feel
pressured, as if they were running some kind of
marriage bureau, with him as the chief victim!

Leaning forward, she told them, 'I feel I
haven't had time to think this thing out
properly, and I really do feel that Richard and I
need to talk it over properly, even though we

both think we know what our decision is going
to be.' There, that should impress him with her
businesslike attitude! He couldn't feel she was
pursuing him with such a harmless suggestion.

She went on, 'I understand Aunt Vi wrote
many books here and I would love to see her
study and the library. I gather it was quite
extensive?'

Her words provoked a response from Paul
she hadn't expected, for he broke in evenly
with, 'Of course, but no doubt you can get all
that done this evening, Shanna? I'm at your
service. We can talk as long as you like. I understand a lift back to the airport has already been
arranged?' He turned to Arthur.

How, thought Shanna, can Paul say that?
Unless, she considered, he had had a talk with
Arthur earlier before he turned up here. Idly
wondering where he had been when he'd
appeared at the gate just now, she shook her
head at his words. 'It took me so long to come
here, Paul, I would feel cheated if I had to go
straight back.'

She smiled brightly. She had been accused of
having a stubborn streak. Not often apparent, it
suddenly surfaced. Why was Paul trying to get
rid of her so hurriedly? It was nothing to do
with him whether she stayed a day or a month.
Until the sale was made, the place was as much
hers as his. Dismayed to find that his attitude
hurt so much, she couldn't help biting her lip.

'My dear Shanna,' began Katerina, 'you're

welcome to stay as long as you like, but,' and here she shot a quick glance at Paul, 'the helicopter will be going out tomorrow and it will be far more convenient if you leave with it than having to get the boat over from Cala Longa.' She turned to Shanna. 'You do understand, don't you, dear?'

'If it's inconvenient, I don't want to put you out,' Shanna replied in her most diplomatic manner, 'but really I quite enjoyed the boat ride and,' she exaggerated, 'I wouldn't miss the return journey for anything.' Only a few hours longer with Paul, that was all she asked. Surely Katerina could see that?

'But think of the problems of getting a cab from Cala Longa,' argued Paul.

She nearly gave up then, but instead shot him daggers and said, 'I'm sure Arthur would ring Santa Eulalia for me, and after all, it won't break the bank, will it?'

There was a lengthy pause. Both Katerina and Arthur seemed to be waiting for Paul to take the lead. Shanna had studied body language and it seemed blatantly obvious they were expecting him to give the orders. The whole situation made her tingle with suspicion.

Paul had told her to trust him. She wanted to trust him. And, when he took her in his arms, she did trust him. But now, when he was sitting opposite her, she felt she couldn't trust him an inch. There was something she was not being told.

With a toss of her head she returned his glance over the guttering candles, challenging him to explain.

Instead he said smoothly, 'Actually, I have business to attend to in Paris, so I must leave first thing tomorrow. I was rather hoping we could sign any official papers tonight and have done with the whole thing as soon as possible. This uncertainty isn't fair on anybody. Metcalf told me he was sending all the official stuff over, and the sooner it's dealt with the better. Was I misinformed?' He frowned and turned to Arthur.

'Not at all, old chap. Everything's ready. I wasn't going to mention it until after the brandy, but I do understand your hurry.' He turned to Shanna. 'If you say your mind is made up?'

She frowned.

Paul stepped in, saying, 'I've managed to combine other business in Europe to make this trip worth while. My time is short, you know.'

'Oh, I see.' Shanna felt suddenly guilty. Here she was trying to squeeze a few extra days for the gratification of her own private amours when Paul was having to fit the whole subject of Tago Mago into a business schedule. 'I'm sorry.' Catching his eye, she gave him a little smile. 'I just didn't realise you were so busy.' It was difficult to keep a shade of irony out of her tones' though' when she added, 'Perhaps you can tell me a little more about your business interests later?' What was it Katerina had said? He earned his living roughing it around the world?

The blond head inclined courteously enough, but, she noticed, he avoided her eye. He's annoyed, she thought. He can't like people messing up his plans. I should have guessed that from the super-efficient way he organised the last leg of my trip here. In a way it was a relief to know he wasn't entirely perfect.

Brandy was served indoors and, true to his word, Arthur produced a sheaf of papers and fully appeared as if he expected Shanna to sign there and then.

'But,' she demurred, 'I would like to talk first.' Fully conscious that both Arthur and Katerina were only employees, she expected them to take the hint and leave, but when they continued to sit there with the obvious intention of sharing in the discussion, she got up, only just managing to conceal her annoyance. 'I really can't sign anything this evening. I need time. In fact,' she went on before anyone could suggest otherwise, 'I shall only sign them when I return to London and have had a word with my own solicitor.'

She got up, placing her empty glass on a side table. 'I wouldn't mind going for a stroll. That was an excellent meal, Katerina, thank you.' Then, fully aware that she was making some sort of exit, she sauntered as slowly as she dared on to the terrace. Let Paul follow or not, she told herself in confusion. But, if he did come out after her, there would be some explaining to do.

She had got as far as the gate when, half turning, she noticed he had come out to stand in the lighted doorway with the other two. Something was said and he left them both, skirting rapidly round the pool towards her.

Still walking slowly, she began to head up the track towards the cove.

'Shanna! I know you've seen me. Wait a moment!'

'Yes, what is it, Richard?' she asked ironically when he caught up with her, then in a sharper tone, 'I notice you answer very easily to your alias. Why do they know you as Paul? Your official name is surely the one used in the will?'

He slipped an arm through hers and walked beside her, matching his pace to her own. 'Everything can be explained, but it's a question of finding the right moment.' He looked down at her flushed face. 'I doubt whether now is the right moment either. You look ready to explode!' He tried to make his tone jocular, but it sounded strained to Shanna's ears and she looked at him strangely. His face had that closed, hurt look again. He frightened her like this, making her quake a little before the kind of contained authority he possessed. He could look so charming in that cool, elegant style of his, like a man at home in hotel bars with a beautiful woman or two on

his arm, but there was also something else, a
hardness that was all male, a kind of physical
toughness, something uncompromising that she
had never met in any man before. She could
guess he would show immense strength of will if
it came to it, and she trembled to think she
might find herself being pitted against it.

'Paul, or Richard——' She paused. 'Tell me
one thing; why are you so keen to sell this lovely
place?'

'I'm not.'

'But——'

'That charade in there—I let it pass because I
don't think Katerina or Arthur realised you
genuinely mistook me for Richard Mather.
Why should they? It was your own mistake.'
His lips compressed. 'I hated letting it go on,
but I could imagine all the questions you might
start asking when you realised your mistake.'

He looked down at her and his blue eyes were
bleak with some unspoken emotion. 'I did ask
you to trust me. I can't explain fully . . . I
don't want to explain, that's closer to the truth.
But you must sell, Shanna. A lot of people are
depending on it.' He paused and said heavily,
'May I ask you to do it as a favour to me?'

She gave a short laugh. 'A favour? Why?
What is all this?'

He shook his head. 'It has to be uncon-
ditional.'

'Do I owe you that sort of favour?' She felt a
sudden panic. Had it all been a way of setting

her up? Paul evidently wanted the island—at least, he wanted her share. What simpler plan than to meet her on the way over here and sweet-talk her into giving it up? For a full minute she was convinced this wild idea was all true. 'A favour? For one or two kisses, perhaps?' Her voice cracked. 'I don't understand you, Paul. Why must I sell?'

'Please, Shanna.' His voice shook, and with a sudden savage movement he dragged her up against his chest, running his hands possessively over her body from thigh to shoulder, allowing his fingers to rake through her hair, finally holding her face between his two hands to enable him to look down into her face with a strength that hurt. The savagery of his emotion set off fires of yearning, dissolving at once the momentary suspicion that his kisses had only been a ploy, and she leaned back, expecting his kiss, longing for it, knowing it would be true.

But he held her for a long moment without moving, her face crushed between his two hands, the play of emotion on his face etching it with deep lines, making him look suddenly old. 'You must do it, Shanna. You must sign those papers tonight.'

Her voice sounded scarcely above a whisper as she asked, 'And if I won't?'

'Then I shall keep you here until you do. Believe me, I can do it.'

His hands slid away from her face after he

spoke, releasing her now that he had exposed a greater hold. It took some minutes for her to realise he was serious.

'Keep me here?' She gave a short laugh. 'For how long?'

'For ever, if need be. Listen, Shanna, it's going to mean nothing for you to sign. You'll make money, don't you realise? What's wrong? Are you sticking out for more? All right, have more. But you must sign.'

'And if I don't,' she finished ironically, 'you'll keep me here for good? Paul,' she ran a hand through her hair, 'all I ask is that you tell me the truth. What is it you're hiding? And how, for heaven's sake, can you promise to pay more?' She stopped suddenly. A thought had struck her. But it didn't seem possible. She turned away. Ahead lay the island, shrouded in night. Arthur's warning came back to her, but the thought of returning to the villa had no appeal either.

She turned back, biting her lip. Suddenly there seemed nowhere to turn. Paul followed her as she began to retrace her steps, then on an impulse she turned again and started to head into the island.

'Listen, Shanna, don't go wandering about here in the dark. Come back with me now. Let's sit down and talk figures.'

'What authority have you to talk figures?' she asked letting the note of derision show. His words of a few moments ago came back. 'I can't even trust you to give me your real name, so how can I believe anything you say about a purchase agreement, which, I should point out, isn't to be made with you at all . . . Is it?' she asked pointedly.

When he didn't answer she turned distractedly towards the lighted villa. It was silly to go rushing off into the night as she felt impelled to do, and she might as well take the lesser of two evils if that was what it was.

Paul followed her, making no attempt to put his arm through hers now.

She still felt trapped by him, and it made her lash out at the nearest victim. 'If you're really in charge, as you seem to be,' she said acidly, 'please will you get rid of those two so we can sit down and talk? I thought they were supposed to be Aunt Vi's employees? They're taking a lot on themselves to join in the discussion, don't you think?'

'They were with her for years. They feel like part of the family.'

'Good for them. Just get rid of them. You'll have to be honest with me, Paul. You tell me to trust you; well, you trust me as well. I don't see what it is you can't tell me.'

'No, but you would if you knew the whole truth.' He spoke half to himself. When she turned his face was haggard. Something about him, despite the harsh expression in which his features were set, made her want to reach out to him. But that same coldness held her back, too. They walked on in silence, both lost in their own thoughts.

When at last they reached the villa again, Katerina and Arthur seemed to have taken the hint, for they were nowhere to be seen.

While Paul poured her a drink, Shanna sat down on one of the loungers beside the pool and watched the lights dancing on the rippling surface. It was just the night for a moonlit swim. The sky, undrained by the glare of city lights, was aswarm with stars.

Paul pulled up a chair beside her. He gave a sigh as if from the depths of his soul. 'Oh, yes,' he murmured, his glance sweeping the scene and finishing on her face, 'I can see why you want to hang on to all this. But think, with the money offered you could find a place with everything you see here——' he waved an arm to include the heavens arching over them, 'and,' he grimaced, his face scarcely relaxing into an attempted smile, 'somewhere on a more convenient route from Gatwick, too.'

'I could do, that's true—if that's what I really wanted. But is it?'

'What?'

'What I really want?'

'You tell me . . . What do you really want, Shanna?' he asked, voice dropping to a husky depth that sent warning shivers up and down her spine.

He knows everything, she thought. He knows precisely how I feel about him. He can even tell that the only reason I'm hanging on here is because I want to hang on to him. Remembering what he had said at dinner, she asked, 'Is it true you're just fitting this into a business trip in Europe?'

He nodded, not really listening. 'I run a world travel organisation,' he told her, bored. 'Diplomats. Top executives. People who need high security.'

'Richard has business in Asia.'

'Richard? You know I'm not Richard,' he told her heavily. 'Why did you think I was?'

She blushed. 'Something Katerina told me.' She was non-committal. 'You seemed to fit the image.' She raised her head. 'Plus you've been talking about getting me to sell up as if you have a vested interest in the place.'

'I have.' He turned away.

'Are you the man who's offered to buy it?'

'One of them.'

'So who are you?'

'Paul Elliot. You already know that.' He smiled bleakly, noting the scepticism in her face. 'You mean, officially who am I?'

She nodded.

'I'm "Inter-Zone Flight-Master"—IZFM to you.'

She gasped. 'Even I've heard of them, and I never travel more than fifty miles outside London.'

'Why not?' He gave her a sharp glance.

'Can't afford the fares or the time,' she

replied, shrugging.

He looked vaguely relieved. 'Is that all? I thought maybe you had some other reason.'

She blinked. 'Has anybody ever told you that you sometimes talk in riddles?'

His mouth quirked at the corners. 'Not in so many words. I'll try to do better in future.' He gave her a tender smile. 'Will you bear with me for a little while? It's important.'

'I guess so. You know, don't you, that you can ask me to do anything, and sooner or later I'll come round to it?' She pulled a face. 'Nobody else can get me to do a thing usually. I'm known for making a fuss and creating havoc——'

'I bet!' he teased. 'Looking at you, I'd say you were the most laid-back lady on Tago Mago.'

'Not difficult,' she quipped. 'I'm probably the only one except for Katerina. But, Paul, joking apart, what are you going to do about Richard? It's all very well getting me to agree to sell to IZFM, but what if he refuses?'

'He won't. He doesn't give a damn.'

'You know him that well?'

'I know him well.'

'You don't like him.'

'Like? Oh, he's affable enough. Maybe I just don't approve of him?'

Shanna felt a quickening of interest. 'Why ever not?'

'He's a bum. Never done a day's work in

his life. Expects everybody to dance attendance on his wishes and whims. It runs in his family——' He broke off, as if having said too much. 'I've told you,' he went on, taking a different line, 'he doesn't care so long as he gets a good price. But Arthur and Katerina, you know, they've both told you, haven't they, how much they want to stay here?'

'So you, out of the kindness of your heart, decide to buy up?'

Paul didn't reply. Instead he leaned across, and she felt a wave of desire as he came close. 'Oh, Paul!' She put up a hand as if to ward him off, her eyes luminous in the glow.

Gently but with the same enigmatic look in his eyes, he stroked her face with one thumb, following the line of forehead and brow, tracing the gentle curve from cheekbone to jaw, smoothing out the little frown lines above the turned-up nose, gently caressing the generous mouth with the tip of a finger. Then, as she knew he would, he slowly began to lower his blond head, and, as she knew she would, she felt her resistance ebb and in a moment she was opening her mouth, yielding to the pressure of his tongue against her own, and reaching up with both hands to pull him down to her. They were both breathing rapidly when he dragged himself away.

'This is rather public, Shanna, and I don't want to hurt you. You're not the type I want to love and leave.'

'Must you?' she cried in a small voice. 'Must you leave me, Paul?'

The bleak look returned and his eyes slid past her, searching among the shadows of night as if an answer could be found there.

'I know you have to go away, but surely it doesn't have to be the end for us?' He played with a tendril of hair on her brow and she said, 'Please, Paul, must it be goodbye?'

He rose to his feet, as if he had come to a sudden decision, reaching down in one movement to pull her up beside him, his face hard. Crushing her against his chest he rasped, 'Tonight you sign the papers. Tomorrow I leave the island with you. We part at the airport. Ask nothing more of me. I beg you, Shanna, ask nothing more. I will ensure you leave here a richer woman than when you arrived.'

With a little cry she wrestled free of his arms and stepped back. 'I won't, Paul. I won't do it!'

'Then you'll have to stay.' With a dark look he strode rapidly away, leaving her beside the pool with her wildly careering thoughts. What did he mean? She would *have* to stay? As a prisoner? But that was absurd.

'Wait!' she cried, but he was already disappearing into the house, his profile a mask of iron.

CHAPTER FIVE

SHANNA'S streak of stubbornness rose to the surface. She would find out what was at the bottom of all this, and she would do it now.

With the intention of finding Paul and having the matter out with him, she got up and hurried inside. A light was burning in the atrium, casting shadows into the corridors that led off it. Pausing to listen for some tell-tale sound that would tell her which way he had gone, she hesitated. A pall of silence hung over the whole villa.

Worried that she might open the wrong door by mistake and disturb someone in bed, she cautiously hurried down the nearest corridor, listening outside the first door she came to for a moment before cautiously turning the knob.

The room was in darkness and plainly Paul was not there. She tried the next door and the next, with the same result, then sped back to one of the other corridors. There were three in all, and only when she came to the third did she find a light on. Expecting to see someone within, she was annoyed to find the room empty. The shutters were open to the night and she got a glimpse of the shiny surface of the pool

through the window before casting her eye
hurriedly over the rest of the room. Evidently
an office—there were all the latest communi-
cation aids imaginable. She began to gape as
her glance slowly took in the equipment. It all
seemed highly powerful for one old lady travel
writer. She frowned. What else was Paul trying
to hide from her? There was surely more to the
place than she had imagined. It almost looked
as if this was a base of operations. But surely he
wouldn't choose to work from a remote place
such as this when there were all the capitals of
the world to choose from?

Looking round, she realised there was no
visible clue to what sort of business was run
from the office, for all that met her gaze were
rows of bland grey plastic machines, metal
cabinets, consoles, banks of telephones,
and—her breath quickened—the only touch of
individuality in the whole place—a photograph
in a plain silver frame on the wall beside the
main keyboard. It was a woman, not more than
twenty-five by the look of her, and Shanna was
half-way across the room, hoping for a closer
look, when she heard the sound of raised voices
outside. Someone was on the terrace. The
voices had lowered, but in the still night air the
words were clearly audible.

'I'll blame you if anything happens to her.' It
was Paul.

'You should have got Arthur to tell Metcalf
she wouldn't be welcome,' a voice she didn't

recognise replied.

'She has a right to come here whenever she wants, but the situation should have been explained.'

'Then why the hell didn't you explain when you had the chance?'

There was a silence.

'Well?' barked the second voice. 'You're capable of sweet-talking a woman, aren't you?'

'You wouldn't understand, Henry.' Paul's voice was rough. It had an immediate effect on the other man.

'Sorry, old man. I know you don't like to broadcast to all and sundry, but if she's a decent sort she'd understand. You'd have her eating out of your hand in no time. After all, what's it to her? She'd never set eyes on the place until today. Right now she's in love with the idea of owning an island. But it'll wear off when she understands the inconvenience. After all, at that age what do they want?'

'What do they want, Henry?' Paul sounded weary.

'Why, the usual, old man. Lights, music— handsome young men at their feet.'

'I'm not exactly in line for my pension myself, Henry. Though God knows, I feel a hundred and ten today. Still, I can quite see I'd be less than ideal for a girl like that.'

The man addressed as Henry gave a soft chuckle. 'I see.' He chuckled richly until Paul broke in with a sharp,

'No, you don't see. I've got my hands full enough with Rowanna, without casting my sights over anyone else.'

But Henry merely chuckled softly to himself as if he had discovered a huge joke he wasn't yet willing to share with anyone.

'You always were a rash young devil, Paul. Glad to see you're adopting a more cautious manner nowadays.'

'Rash? You're right, not any longer. And surely even you can't say I haven't been cautious enough over the last few years.'

'Sorry.' Henry sounded genuinely apologetic. 'Never quite sure what you get up to when you're away. 'Nor,' he added warningly, 'is Rowanna.'

She has nothing to worry about. She knows she comes first. Always will.'

Shanna knew her knuckles were turning white only when she happened to glance down at them. She released her grip on the edge of the window-frame, bitterly regretting that she had accidentally overheard this brief snatch of conversation, but before she could shut out the sound she heard Paul say quite loudly, 'But none of this solves our real problem, Henry. How in hell do we get her to sign the island over?'

'Would she consider a leasehold on the buildings? Promise her a summer villa on the beach. Somewhere she can bring her friends in the holidays. I'm sure you could swing a deal like that, old man, if you really wanted to.'

Shanna turned blindly from the window. She could hear Paul's murmured response, but she felt ashamed to have listened so long. It had been difficult to break away when she herself was the subject—she and some woman called Rowanna.

Opening the door of the office, and not caring whether anyone heard her or not, she made her way back to the atrium and crossed towards the terrace. Paul was already walking up towards the gates, a large torch in his hands swinging from side to side, casting a bright beam on the path in front of him.

Her high heels tapped on the paving stones and a figure on one of the pool-side seats turned sharply at the sound.

'You must be Henry,' she remarked coldly as she drew level, then before the astonished man could get to his feet she ran quickly across the terrace after Paul. Even before she called his name he was turning, evidently having heard her footsteps behind him.

'My God, so there you are! I thought you'd gone careering off into the night again.'

'You didn't seem in too much of a hurry to go after me,' she observed caustically, remembering the lengthy discussion that had just taken place outside the office window.

'I knew you wouldn't go far in the dark. I was worried, though, that you might veer off the path and break your neck in one of the ravines.'

'Thanks for the thought.'

'What's the matter? You look furious.'

'Do I? Why on earth should I?' Forgetting the observer beside the pool, she went on, 'I've no reason to be furious. After all, I've just inherited a part-share in a Mediterranean island with the head of an international company threatening either to run me off it or keep me prisoner. All in the day's work for someone like you, I suppose. Nothing to feel cross about, no, not at all!' Her voice had risen and she knew she wasn't making sense by the puzzled frown that appeared on Paul's face.

He stepped forward and she flinched, exclaiming, 'Keep your hands off me! I'm not as easy as all that to talk round. Despite your evident prowess, Mr Elliot, at the persuading game.'

She wanted to hit him. He was standing motionless with that look of icy aloofness on his face that made her feel so helpless. It was as if nothing she said would be received in the way in which she meant it. He obviously thought she was a monumental nuisance, but someone over whom he could assert his will at any time.

'I'm just a minor irritation to you, aren't I? Go on! Say it! Have a good laugh—your plan misfired and instead of the island you've got—you've got——' Dashing a hand across her face she turned and ran blindly past him up the track into the darkness.

'Shanna! Come back!'

She slowed, feeling melodramatic to be running away like this, but too distraught to want to return to face him. He came up beside her.

'I've got what?' he demanded.

'Nothing,' she choked back, trying to walk away.

'We seem to be doing a lot of this, don't we?'

'What?'

'Misunderstanding each other.'

'There's no misunderstanding,' she exclaimed, her lips trembling. 'Only one or two blanks to be filled in.' She turned to look squarely into her face. 'I understand you very well now, thank you very much. Have no fears.'

'Shanna, Shanna . . .' His voice dropped to a whispered caress and he reached out towards her. She saw his hand illuminated in the light from the torch before the beam swung away, then warm fingers were holding her wrist and she tried to snatch her arm out of reach, but he tightened his grasp saying, 'No, I'm not letting you go like that. You'll explain that little outburst, and you'll let me put things straight. I hate to see you like this.'

'Don't give me that, you heel,' she uttered, still struggling half-heartedly to get away. 'No doubt you've already thought of a suitable story——' she stifled a sob '—but it won't work. I told you I wanted time. And now I'm even more determined to hang on for as long as I can.'

There wasn't a shred of truth in it, but the thought that her feelings weren't returned, despite the conviction with which he begged her to trust him, and despite the wonder of his lovemaking, drove her to say things she didn't mean.

'Stubborn.' He laughed softly and evidently he didn't believe her.

She could just make out his face in the darkness and she saw a flash of white teeth, then his lips closed and he was bringing her close into the crook of his arm, turning her back towards the villa with the words, 'Let's cool it, shall we? I think the time has come to set the record straight as far as I can. But I must warn you, there are one or two things I find it difficult to talk about.'

'You're going to ask for my co-operation?' she asked, letting him lead her back towards the lights.

'Yes.'

'For co-operation read capitulation,' she added bitterly.

He paused. 'Let's not prejudge the outcome. You're a free agent.'

She halted at the gates. 'I'm not as stupid as you seem to think. If you imagine all it takes is a bit of flattery, then you couldn't be more wrong. I know I'm a free agent without you telling me so. And I'm not open to pressure. From anyone.' She surprised herself with the firmness of her words. Glancing at Paul's expression, she saw something in it like respect. Or open surprise at such bluntness coming from a mere girl.

'I respect your point of view,' he told her, confirming her first impression, 'but wait until you know some of the problems you've set us before you make a decision. And Shanna,' he slid his hand down her bare arm as he released her, 'I don't want you to try to make a decision before tomorrow morning. Come along,' he said over his shoulder, 'let's discuss this like rational human beings.'

Aghast at the prospect his words conjured up, she followed nervously behind. If he thought she was going to stay up all night, pretending to discuss the pros and cons with him, when his whole intention was to persuade her to do what he wanted in the end anyway . . . her cheeks blazed. There was the extra danger of spending the long night hours alone . . .

'I hope I misunderstood you back there,' she said as soon as they reached the lighted terrace again. When he raised his eyebrows for an explanation, she blushed, adding hastily, 'My day started about four a.m. I was hoping for a nice long sleep at some point before tomorrow.'

'I'm sure that can be arranged.' He gave her a teasing look. 'You can stay on here, you know. Nobody's going to expect you to get the nine o'clock boat in the morning.'

'I thought it was arranged,' she said stiffly.

'Anything can be unarranged. Don't worry.'

'Even the helicopter link to the airport?'

'I'm sorry—I was trying to pressure you. I shall be piloting it myself, so there's no problem there either.'

'No, the only problem is me, isn't it?' She sat down on the chair he pulled out for her. Music came floating from inside the house and Paul's companion from a few minutes ago came shuffling out again.

He was an old man in his late seventies, she saw now, but despite the silvery hair he was tall, well built, bronzed, and cosmopolitan in an expensive white suit and silk cravat. He was lighting up a cigar and held it in his left hand as he reached out to offer Shanna his right in greeting with old-world courtesy.

'My dear, so good to meet you at last,' he greeted her as if they hadn't already encountered each other. 'I'm Henry Denfield, Vi's fourth husband. She spoke often of your poor dear mother. Quite her favourite in the collection,' he told her.

'That must be why she left this place to me. I didn't expect it.'

'Neither, my dear, did any of us.'

'So I gather,' she said shortly, with an unforgiving glance in Paul's direction.

Henry followed her glance. 'Shall I——?' He waved the cigar.

'No, stay,' replied Paul, interpreting the

gesture. 'You may be able to account for Vi's eccentricities better than I.'

'Ha!' Henry took a seat and frowned slightly. 'There'll never be her like again.' His eyes held a look of genuine pain, and Shanna guiltily remembered that it was only two months since his wife's death.

'I only met her once. When I was three. It was in London. I scarcely remember her. I think we had ice-cream. It was green and blue. I'd never seen anything like that before.'

'That's Vi. Always providing surprises.'

'Huh! You can say that again!' It was Paul. Shanna gave Henry an apologetic look. 'Mother loved her, but she died when I was still at school, so I never really got to know Aunty Vi. Somehow this all seems like a dream.' She cast an eye over the pool and the white walls of the Villa Mimosa. 'It's as if some fairy godmother has suddenly appeared and waved a wand for me——' She stumbled, hoping she was making sense.

So far Paul had been listening with a sceptical expression since his brief outburst, but now he leaned forward. 'Fairy godmother, yes, you're exactly right, Shanna.' He patted Henry on the knee. 'Right, Henry? That's it exactly. I always knew she reminded me of something.'

'That's all right if the gift is welcome, old man, but you can't go around playing games like that without taking into account all the consequences.' He turned to Shanna. 'As you've discovered, this bequest of Vi's has put a regular cat among the pigeons.' His eyes flicked to Paul as if to reassure him about something. 'Paul here——' he paused '—well, he runs a group of companies from the island. It'd be an upheaval for him to relocate, for one. And me, well, I'm an old man with a backlog of memories. Lived here with Vi for years. A place where we've grown old together. Sorry to leave it.' His voice trailed away.

'But why did she do it? That's what I don't understand. She must have known how you all felt about leaving here?'

Henry laughed. 'There was method in her madness. She knew what she was doing all right. Me—well, she had this crazy idea I'd be better off on the mainland, putting a little project of mine into being. And Paul here——' he broke off '—well,' he said as some sort of unspoken warning was issued, 'she had her reasons there too, no doubt.' He cleared his throat and pretended to relight his cigar.

Shanna remembered what Katerina had said about Vi's hopes for herself and Richard. Things hadn't worked out, though. Paul had stepped into her life instead. She wondered what reason Vi had for wanting to release Paul himself from the island. A look at his face now told her nothing.

Feeling guilty to be the unwitting instrument of Vi's machinations, Shanna knew she would have to reassure Henry, as well as, to her greater reluctance, Paul too, should they be completely sure they wanted to go against Vi's wishes. She could understand their reluctance to obey a request from beyond the grave. Vi must have been an autocratic lady, right enough. But Shanna had no intention of upsetting anyone. First, though, she had to ask a few questions about her co-owner, questions she hadn't got around to asking Katerina.

'Who is Richard Mather? Why do you think Vi left the place to us both?'

'There's a family connection,' broke in Paul before Henry could open his mouth. 'Not between you and him, of course——' He broke off. 'He used to spend holidays here. With his sister. He still visits from time to time.'

'Once in a blue moon,' added Henry. He leaned forward, 'You won't mind me saying this, but she was a dreadful matchmaker. Knowing how her mind works, she'd be hoping to give you more than an island.' He chuckled. 'She'd be thinking he'd make you good husband material. It wouldn't enter her head that you might already have a boyfriend you intended to set up house with——'

'I haven't,' she answered shortly, deliberately avoiding Paul's glance. She would demand to hear his story when Henry left them.

Stifling a yawn, she went on, 'Now you've filled me in on the situation it's making sense, but,' she frowned, 'I still don't see why I wasn't told all this in the first place. This mysterious buyer Mr Metcalf first mentioned? It was you, Paul.'

'Yes. But it wasn't relevant at that stage to explain all the ins and outs of it. Since then there's been someone else on the scene. We don't know who he is, but we're certainly in a position to match whatever he's going to offer.' Paul sounded bored by the whole business, as if he wanted her questions to come to an end as soon as possible. His clipped tones told her that he still clung to his original intention.

'I know I said I wouldn't capitulate,' Shanna replied, 'but it's obvious I have to, isn't it? You want me to offer you first refusal?'

'That's the long and short of it.' Henry blew a smoke ring and watched it float off into the night.

'And Richard?'

Henry frowned. 'If I know Richard, he'll make no such promise. He'll sell to the highest bidder. We could land ourselves in a Dutch auction situation.'

'And is that what you thought I would do if I discovered how much you needed the place yourselves?'

Paul looked away, but didn't answer.

Henry got up. 'You were a bit of an unknown quantity, my dear, and Metcalf has been pushing the claims of this other buyer quite strongly, I gather. I always told Vi to put matters into other hands, but he's a first cousin of number one husband, something like that, and she seemed to feel she ought to let him handle her property affairs. Frankly, her relationships were positively Byzantine. It's going to take an army of lawyers to sort out the rest of the claims on her estate. There'll be some fat wallets among the wig and gown brigade after the last document is signed, believe me!' Chuckling genially, he excused himself then and, wishing them both goodnight, made his way indoors.

'We'd better follow his example,' suggested Paul, 'you're yawning your head off.'

Shanna flushed at the 'we', glad of the concealing darkness. 'Yes, I am tired,' she agreed.

Feeling a little perplexed by events, she rose to her feet. What did the island matter anyway? Or Vi's matchmaking ambitions, come to that? She had only toyed with the idea of keeping it on because Paul was here. But she wouldn't want it, wouldn't even want to lease it to his company, so long as he was going to be here with some other woman. All the way through the conversation with Henry the one thought had been hammering away in the background. She felt her spirits drag.

'Shanna . . .' Paul's voice was like velvet. 'I'm sorry about the lack of frankness. It seemed worth letting it pass if things could be settled quickly. I hadn't bargained on the new owner being someone like you.' He paused.

'For what it's worth, everything else I've told you is true.'

'What?' She spun sharply, her hand groping for the back of a chair. Her eyes searched for his, but his face was in shadow, his expression hidden.

Then he rose quickly to his feet and came over to her. 'Don't look like that. I've hurt you. I'm so sorry. It's the last thing I——'

'You haven't hurt me,' she lied, averting her face.

'Then why are you looking like that?'

'Like what?' she replied in a choky voice, then more strongly, adding, 'If I'm hurt, I've hurt myself, for being so impressionable. I haven't done much travelling,' she went on as if that explained something.

He laughed gently, putting one hand on her shoulder in a gesture which, because it was a way of showing sympathy, brought a lump to her throat. Sympathy was the last thing she wanted. She shook it off. 'I'm going in.'

'Goodnight. God bless.'

She tried to reply but the words were locked in. All she could do was give a little shrug, then, turning, not quite seeing anything in front of her, she made her way rapidly inside, searching blindly for a minute or two for the door of her room and, when she found it, throwing herself down on the bed with a stifled sob.

How was it possible to feel like this? No one she had ever met measured up to Paul. But it was obvious she could have no part in his life, and he had never intended that she should. There was the woman in the photograph in pride of place in his office. She hadn't been mentioned. But that was only one more example of 'lack of frankness' to contend with.

She was out of her element with him, that was the trouble. Her feelings were careering from one direction to another. Meeting him had been like a forest fire—one moment there was nothing, then suddenly there was a spark and the next a conflagration burning everything in its path.

There was a knock on her door.

'Yes?' she called, hearing her voice crack and having to repeat the invitation to enter.

It was Paul. He was holding her evening-bag. 'You left this.' He held it out.

'Oh, God . . .' Her face crumpled. 'I'm so tired,' she muttered, trying to excuse herself as she felt him come across the room and kneel down beside her. 'I'm just so tired.'

He stroked her hair. 'I'll get you a drink. I jet all over the place. I'd forgotten it can be a bit of a strain if you're unused to it. Wait here.'

He went out and Shanna, after an ineffectual protest, waited for him to return, smoothing her hair in the mirror and pointlessly checking her make-up. He would bring her drink, then go back to his Rowanna, whoever she was. Their room must be in one of the other corridors, but where was she this evening? Was she away? Was that why Paul had taken such risks, holding her in his arms, kissing her on the beach where anyone could have strolled up to the clifftop and witnessed them?

He came in with a mug of hot milk. 'There's brandy in it. You'll sleep like a top.'

'Paul,' she said as he turned to go, 'who else lives here?'

'At the villa? Only Arthur and Katerina and the cook.'

'And Henry?'

He paused. 'No, actually. He——' he hesitated, 'he's in the main house, Vi's old place, on the other side of the island. It's called the Villa Torres.'

'You mean there's more than one villa on the island?'

'Yes.'

'Two, then?'

He shrugged. Then, as if having regretted holding out on her even for a moment longer, he said, 'Three, actually.'

'The third being yours?'

He nodded.

She took a deep breath. Her fingers felt like ice. 'And you live there with your wife, do you? Or is she just a girlfriend?' She raised her face, watching him, half expecting him to tell her to mind her own business.

He didn't flinch, though, looking her straight in the eyes and saying, 'Wife, actually.'

'I see.'

'No, you don't see, Shanna! You don't see at all.' He bent down and gripped her by the back of the neck. 'Who's been talking to you? Who is it? Tell me?' His face was flushed with anger, his eyes sparking.

'Does it matter?' she replied hotly. 'Does it really matter?' She struggled wildly to free herself from his grasp, but he was determined not to let her go.

'What have you found out about her?' he demanded hoarsely, his fingers clawing into the back of her neck.

'My God,' she explained in as dignified a voice as she could muster, 'you *are* upset! Why should it bother you that I've discovered your nasty little deception? What's the matter? Does it spoil the image of honest Joe you were hoping to create? Poor Paul! I never guessed you were going to be so wild about being found out!'

'Shut up, Shanna! What are you saying?'

'Do you make a habit of going around seducing disco-loving tourists, then? Is it a hobby? Poor Rowanna. At least she can see her photograph in your office and feel you're thinking of her every time you go to work.' She gave a hard laugh. 'You can obviously manage to pull the wool over her eyes, but thank goodness you can't do it with me!'

Her own blue eyes searched his face, noting the drawn look, evidence, she judged, of guilt. She gave another hard laugh, if only to stop herself from crying.

'She must take one look at your face and be able to read your guilt off it like reading a page of a book,' she bit out. 'I've never seen anyone look so guilty at being found out.'

'Maybe because I'm not used to it,' he snapped back.

'Being found out?'

'Lying,' he snarled. Deep in his eyes there was a look of puzzlement mingled with something that might have been mistaken for relief, but, if that was what it was, it made no sense to Shanna.

'Listen to me, idiot, you don't know anything,' he said on a different note, his fingers still grasping her by the nape but becoming gentler, caressing it. 'I asked you to trust me. I'll ask you again. And I'll say this. Whatever the outcome of the sale of Tago Mago, we shall meet again. That's a promise. Having found you, I'm not going to give you up easily.'

She gazed at him in stupefaction. Her face crimsoned. 'Thanks for nothing. Are you serious? You think I'd contemplate a sordid little affair on the side? What sort of scheming type do you think I am? What's more important, *why* do you think that? It's grossly insulting!'

'Wait, listen to me——'

'Don't you dare fill my ears with any more lies and false promises. Don't you dare! And, take your hands off me. I hate you, you——'

'Shanna,' his voice was soft, 'Shanna . . .' He shook his head. 'What I promise, I mean—today, tomorrow and forever.'

With that he got to his feet, gradually releasing her, and, with a look that seemed empowered to squeeze her heart into a ball of pain, he went slowly from the room.

CHAPTER SIX

SHANNA couldn't sleep. The moonlight travelled a path from one side of the window to the other as she lay awake through the silent hours, watching it. Lying stiffly under the single blanket for as long as she could, she eventually flung herself out of bed with a cry of exasperation and went over to the window to lean out.

It was a night made for love: warm, flower-scented, the air disturbed only by a light breeze freshening from the sea. Stars scattered the pathways of heaven, stars lovers could spend their lives counting.

In the darkness the pool gave only a hint of silver as the breeze stirred its surface with the lightest breath.

Well, why not? she thought, driven on impulse by inner pain. I won't get another chance . . .

With this desolate thought she was sent slithering over the window-sill to tread a silent path to the water's edge, then, naked, she lowered herself into the cool depths. A little gasp as its cold fingers tickled her ribs was the only sound before she began to ripple with smooth, leisurely strokes across the calm surface, the pain of the last few hours momentarily banished by the pleasure of the lapping waters caressing her bare skin.

When she touched the other side she turned, intending to swim back, but a slight movement out of the corner of her eye made her turn her head. She gave a gasp. Something blurry passed her line of vision. Then suddenly she was looking up the long length of a man's body encased in white trousers and an open-necked shirt, and even before her startled glance reached his face she guessed at once who it was.

It was Paul Elliot. And he had a face filled with fury.

Why he was so angry she didn't have time to find out. 'What the hell do you think you're doing? Get out!' he snarled. He swivelled, and for a moment she thought he had simply gone inside. But in a moment he returned with a large white beach-towel, holding it out like a wind-break, and, it seemed, fully expecting her to climb out and wrap herself up in it.

She swam lazily back into the middle of the pool. 'Do what?' she called from her vantage point of relative safety.

'You heard.' He sounded less angry, but no less peremptory.

'I think you said, get out, but as I'm not in the habit of obeying irrational orders without question, I'm afraid I feel disinclined to comply.' She swam a few more strokes, then lay back, kicking her legs idly in front of her. He seemed to be in a towering rage, only mitigating his earlier uncalled-for instructions with the obvious need to appease her if he wanted to get her to do as he ordered. Obviously he realised this. She smiled grimly. If she wanted to swim naked at midnight, that was her decision.

'Shanna,' he began patiently, 'it's not a good idea to swim alone in the middle of the night when you've been drinking.'

'Have I been drinking?'

'Probably more than you're used to.'

'Oh, but we disco girls drink an awful lot!' she mocked. 'Please don't imagine I don't know what I'm doing.'

'I expect you always know that,' he replied coldly. 'Why are you teasing me like this?'

'Am I?'

'You know you are.'

'Then put that silly towel down and come and join me,' she challenged.

She expected him to throw in the towel, probably literally, and stomp off. Instead he stood watching her for a moment, his expression difficult to guage in the moonlight, then, to her astonishment, he slowly began to strip. First the shirt, ripped off over the head and flung to one side, then the shoes, and then the belt of his white trousers, snapping audibly as he unbuckled it and snaking away through his fingers as he dropped that too to the ground.

She saw his hand hover over his zip, then there was a sharp rasp as he pulled it down. She watched, unable to tear her eyes away as his trousers slid over muscular, tanned legs to the tiles. He was wearing very brief white boxer shorts. They stood out starkly against the deep even brown of his magnificent physique.

She waited, holding her breath. Then, with a chuckle, he called softly across the water, 'You should know me well enough by now to realise I never resist a challenge, especially coming from the lips of a water nymph.' And with a deft flick of his wrist he slid out of the shorts and threw them to join the rest of his things.

Before she could move he was plunging into the pool in a graceful arc, entering the water as smoothly as an arrow, and then she saw the approaching ripples as he moved powerfully under the surface towards her.

Some primitive fear made her thrash frantically to get out of his reach, but she reckoned without his superior speed. She felt his hands snatch at her legs, then they were slithering up her thighs and he was pulling her down under the water with him, hands twining around her waist, in her hair, a confusion of arms and legs threshing to the surface where, gasping and spluttering, she tried in vain to wriggle from out of his clutches.

He caught her strongly round the waist again, and even while she still struggled vainly to free herself he swam with her to the edge of the pool. There, dragging her up the shallow steps, drops of water cascading from his shoulders in the moonlight, he pulled her out of the water, the air striking warm as a caress on her naked flesh, making his warmer touch merge into the night with a dizzying of her senses. It made her long to yield to the force of his apparent intention.

'I told you to get out, and I mean what I say. So if you won't come when asked, you should expect this method——' he murmured huskily, making it a game as if to deny the reality, the all too apparent reality, of his desire.

When she didn't answer he laughed softly. 'You're not so sparky now you're in my power,' he remarked, teasing, bringing his face into her hair and dragging her unprotesting body against his hard-muscled one. Shanna felt as if she would faint. The white heat of desire swept through her, wiping everything else from her mind.

But it was Paul holding her in an attitude ready for lovemaking, Paul, who was married to someone else.

The thought made her struggle madly, kicking out with bare feet and biting and scratching any piece of naked flesh she could find. At first, taken by surprise, his hold slipped, until, provoked by what he misconstrued as an attack, he gripped her more roughly, twisting her arms behind her back, holding the thrashing legs tight against his own so she was almost immobilised.

'That's not fair, it's a judo hold,' she panted, wondering what he was going to do next now he had her in his power, and breathing rapidly in anticipation as the length of his body covered her own with its burning heat. Her whole frame was trembling, yearning towards him, but she was determined never to yield.

'I know a lot more than judo holds, so just keep still,' he rasped. Then, in a different tone, he added, 'Don't worry, I get the message. And it's no. With regret.'

'Arrogant devil.'

'Regret on both sides, Shanna.' He muffled his face in her hair again and gave a harsh groan. She felt him shudder with thwarted desire as she turned in his arms.

'If I let you go, do you promise to cover yourself up at once like a good girl? I don't think I can take any more, and I warn you, I won't let you go unless you promise.' His voice shook with the strain of holding back his natural desire.

'I haven't much choice, have I?' she groaned, feeling as if the world was spinning and vibrating beneath her feet with the power of her resistance. She felt him slide away, slowly, holding her as her melting limbs refused to take her weight, catching her once as she stumbled, then stepping back as she regained her balance.

'Towel,' he prompted, bending to retrieve it.

She pulled it haphazardly around herself.

'No, like this.' He reached out, folding it tightly over her breasts and tucking it so that it couldn't open accidentally. 'I never knew I could stand so much,' he said huskily, stepping back as if it took an effort to keep his hands off her. 'Do you always sail this close to the wind?' He laughed before she could answer. 'Go, please, Shanna. I know you'd regret it in the morning if I did what I wanted to do with you. Please, baby,' he repeated, 'don't push me . . . The way you're looking now, you don't seem to realise what you're doing to me. Either that or you get your kicks this way.' His mouth twisted, humour vying with frustrated hunger.

She walked slowly out of range, sneaking a look back at him, wondering what she would do if he followed, and wondering, equally, what she was going to do when he didn't.

If she had failed to find sleep so far tonight, the rest of the night was going to be an even bigger failure.

She reached her room, closing her door and leaning her forehead against it. Listening for the sound of his footsteps. Hearing nothing. Wondering where he was, whether he had gone back to his wife. Wondering, now there was time to think, what he had been doing, sitting out by the pool by himself through the night. Both of them sleepless. But for the same reason? She wanted to believe it. But the ugly thought that he was a married man hammered at her heart, making it bleed.

Morning couldn't come soon enough. Exhausted, Shanna crawled from the tangled covers and made her way to the shower. Unrefreshed by it, made weak with anticipation, she dressed carefully in a pair of casual beige trousers and a plain cotton top and made her way down to the kitchen. She knew it was time for breakfast because she had heard Cook clashing pans. A cup of coffee was all she wanted.

Relieved of the necessity to make conversation by the woman's busyness in the kitchen, she went outside. Already the sun was hot. With no particular plan, she decided the best thing in her present state of mind was to go for a good, brisk walk. Besides, she was curious to see the rest of what was still her island before she lost it for good. Somewhere in her mind she knew she wanted a look at the other two villas.

Taking a cliff path different from the one she knew led to the rickety bridge over the ravine, she set off energetically, pleased to see no one and guessing that Arthur, if not Katerina too, was still in bed.

The sea crawled at the foot of the cliffs like a sleeping monster, belying its power, the wrinkled blue expanse like skin moving over bunched muscles. Her mind flew to Paul's smooth, muscular, bronzed perfection . . . No, she told herself, giving her arm a pinch. Forget him. He's not for you.

The enigma of his life taunted her, daring her to prise its secrets from it. She felt that if she could only see his life in its day-to-dayness he would lose his mystery, his power over her. She had never met anyone like him, could never hope to. His coolness, his fire, taunted her. The enigma she sensed at the heart of him. His sudden sadness.

And above all else his words of love: today, tomorrow and forever. Those were the ones she remembered. Only common sense told her they were merely words.

Reaching the top of the cliffs without noticing anything, so enrapt in thoughts of Paul was she that she began the descent and was part of the way down before she noticed a villa perched precariously on the cliff-edge below. It was surrounded by a walled garden, and there was a pool, clearly visible, a large sweep of curving terrace littered with chairs, a table, and— Shanna slowed her pace—a lone figure sitting at a table, breakfasting, she observed, a coffee-pot, a cup and saucer, everything clearly visible from above.

'Rowanna,' she said aloud. It must be. Dark hair, long, tied back in a bright scarf, dark glasses, a thin, tanned face, bracelets glinting in the strong sunlight. As she watched, the woman rose to her feet and, holding the coffee-pot carefully in front of her, made her way indoors.

Shanna moved a pace or two down the slope, wondering if she had been observed. It was

crazy to go back now. The woman would have
seen her. If she didn't go on she would look like
a spy. Heart in mouth, she traced the faint
indentation that was the path until she was a few
hundred yards away. Still the way was steep
enough to enable her to see over the stone wall
surrounding the garden.

The women re-emerged from the house,
coffee-pot held carefully between her hands. She
seemed to be deep in thought, or dreaming,
standing for a moment, the pot still held in front
of her, her eyes fixed on the horizon, sitting
carefully at last, pausing, then thoughtfully,
dreamily, pouring a jet of coffee into her cup.

Now she was closer Shanna could see how
thin she was, her loose smock hanging in
billowing folds about the gaunt figure. A little
closer and she drew in her breath. There were
purplish scars down the side of the woman's
face. She turned her head, looking away to
where the sea danced beneath the cliff, and
Shanna wondered if she had imagined those
livid marks destroying the woman's beauty. She
hesitated a moment, willing the woman to turn
back so she could see whether she had been
imagining it or not. And then again the woman
turned, revealing them to her appalled scrutiny.

Shanna's breath was released in a long sigh of
pity. Her thoughts flew to Paul, the underlying
sadness in his eyes, his unexplained reticence
about his private life.

She turned away. Was this what he had been

trying to hide? Had she now unwittingly stumbled upon his secret?

In a confusion of pity and horror at what she had seen, she set off on a path that took her round the back of the villa. She would walk on. It was a way of clearing her head.

Paul, she thought. Paul. My love. Dear love.

He seemed more unattainable than ever, their games last night trivial, her own pain an indulgence. After her walk she would try to get Arthur to bring the papers to her. She would sign without further delay.

It was obvious now why Paul was so desperate to keep the island. It was his wife's personal sanctuary. Her safe place in a world which would only offer pity or indifference.

After signing away her gift, she would ask Arthur to help her get off the island. It would never do to meet Paul now she knew his secret. She would return to London. There would never be anything but heartache if she remained on Tago Mago.

CHAPTER SEVEN

SHE made her way along a path that led through a small stand of pines behind the villa and, reluctant to return before she had managed to sort out her feelings, she walked on up the next hill, puffing slightly as she reached the summit. She could understand why the island had so few domestic buildings, given its geography of short, steep hills, craggy red cliffs and few beaches. It would serve as an ideal hideaway for anyone who no longer wanted to be part of life.

Her eyes saddened at the thought of Paul, so vital, at the height of his powers, having to spend his life in a place like this, away from the dynamic centre of things where he rightly belonged. He must love Rowanna very much.

Fighting back her own unhappiness, which seemed trivial by comparison, she gazed out over the view revealed from her vantage point at the summit of the hill. Below was a flat, green headland, markers indicating that this was the helicopter landing-pad. A thin trail led up into the rocks on the far side and she guessed that it would probably take her back to her starting point. Now she could guess why Paul had tried to stop her crossing the bridge yesterday. It would have brought her out within sight of Rowanna's hideaway.

She could tell she'd reached the farthest end of the small island, and Aunty Vi's house, the Villa Torres, must lie somewhere over the next headland.

More for something to do to keep her mind off Paul and Rowanna than from curiosity, Shanna set off at a jog across the flat green turf, wondering where the helicopter was this morning, not having heard it take off. But only when she came to a stop at the foot of the path did she register that of course Paul had said something about leaving. He had simply set off far earlier than she had anticipated. She wondered if it was Paris as he had suggested: then the realisation struck her that if she left today as she intended they would probably never meet again.

The thought momentarily blacked all else from her mind. She flung herself down on to the grass, pulling her knees up under her chin and gripping them tightly as if to hold on to something safe, then tears glistened on her cheeks—the blue sky, sweep of green, the cliffs with their coronet of sea-birds, all became blurred under a mist of tears.

Eventually she got to her feet, dashing a hand across her eyes as she did so. That's that, she told herself. I'm calm again now. I can cope. I'll go back to London. Sadder but wiser. She smiled bitterly to herself. Maybe it was all part of growing up. To discover that one couldn't always have what one would give one's life for.

It took a good three quarters of an hour to return to the Villa Mimosa, after gingerly skirting the promontory on which the more splendid Villa Torres was perched and braving the rickety wooden bridge over the ravine where she had met Paul.

Vi's villa had been the epitome of luxury living, even more lavish than the one on the other side of the island, but she couldn't help thinking how lonely Henry would be, living in such spectacular isolation. Perhaps as far as her plans for Henry were concerned, Vi had been right. He would be better off on the mainland with companions of a similar type.

As for Rowanna—well, it seemed callous to thrust a woman as disfigured as that unwillingly into the outside world.

Arthur came out as soon as she appeared.

'I've been looking everywhere for you, dearie. Everything all right?' He eyed her pale face with concern.

'Fine. I've just been for a walk. I thought I should see the rest of the island—for the first and last time,' she added, giving a rueful shrug.

'Desolate, isn't it?' he remarked. 'You ought to look at property on the mainland. Much

more your style. If I were twenty years
younger——' He smiled disarmingly. 'Anyway, enough of that. The boat's coming out as
soon as this wind drops.'

For the first time Shanna noticed that away
from the sheltered easterly coast there was a
distinct on-shore breeze on this side. Out in the
channel the wind would be much fiercer. 'When
is it likely to get here?' she asked, thinking she
might as well do what little packing there was to
be done straight away.

'That's anybody's guess. We're often holed
up here for weeks.' He seemed unperturbed
by the thought and turned back towards the
house.

'Arthur! Do you seriously mean that?'

He laughed when he saw her worried face. 'I
doubt whether it's going to be too bad at this
time of year. But there's no telling. It could be a
day or so, if this gale they're forecasting does
come up.'

'Gale?'

He had gone busily off, and only turned with
a helpless shrug when he heard the sound of
dismay in her voice.

'Plenty to keep you amused here, don't
worry,' he called. 'Go and browse in Vi's
library. That's what you wanted, isn't it?
Or——' he came back '—we've plenty of videos
here if you don't want to walk all that way
again.'

'Thank you,' she murmured, making a

gradual mental readjustment. What about her flight from Malaga? Would she have to cancel it and sit it out until another one turned up? That would mean taking a room in a hotel when she reached the mainland. Unexpected expense. Would her funds run to it? She remembered Paul's words telling her that he would make sure she left the island a richer woman than when she came. Running a hand through her hair, she followed Arthur indoors.

The wind did get up later that morning, and it was obviously going to be impossible to leave as planned. Following Arthur's suggestion, Shanna made herself comfortable in the games-room, a long, single-storey attachment to the main block, and chose at random from the shelves of videos on display. Neither Arthur nor Katerina joined her and she felt as lonely as if she had the whole island to herself.

If they're trying to give me a taste of what it would be like to live here—and hoping to put me off—they've succeeded, she thought morosely as the hours lagged by. At about half-past three, after a solitary lunch in a sheltered corner of the terrace, she heard the roar of the approaching helicopter.

Longing and fearing to hear it in equal measure, she went to the french windows and stood there looking up. It was so low that she could see Paul in the pilot's seat. He was alone. Perhaps Henry had had to be taken back to wherever he had been the previous day. One thing was for sure, Paul hadn't yet left for Paris.

He appeared about an hour later. By this time, rain was streaming down the windows as if it would never stop. His blond hair was slicked flat to his head, his face wet, his cotton shirt bundled damply in one hand as he strode across the terrace. Thinking she was unseen, Shanna watched him go through the door on the far side. Her heart had quickened at the sight of that powerful back and shoulders, wet with rain, shinily tactile, asking to be touched.

A moment after he disappeared there was a sound at the games-room door. It opened and suddenly he was standing there, staring in at her. She jumped to her feet, then froze where she was in confusion, quelling the impulse to go into his arms that his sudden presence had provoked.

'I see you didn't get away. I wasn't sure.' He came into the room after closing the door behind him. He had picked up a large towel from somewhere and rubbed his hair with it before slinging it over his shoulders. Its fluffy whiteness made him look like a soapflake ad. Or a champion boxer in one of those American movies, she thought, holding her breath as he came closer.

'Have you got a drink?'

'N-no,' she replied, unable to tear her eyes from him.

'I'll get you one. What would you like?'

'Anything. It doesn't matter, I—I'm just surprised to see you,' she muttered, trying to excuse her confusion. She had expected him to go to Rowanna first.

'So I see. You look as if you've seen a ghost. Watching something scary?' He nodded towards the video set.

'I don't know.' She gave a shaky laugh. 'It's just on. I'm not really watching.'

He picked up the controls and turned down the sound. 'I thought you'd have left by now. The weather too bad for the boat to come out?'

She nodded.

'Fate.' His face was chiselled in an attitude of resignation. He went to the cabinet and poured two large brandies. 'I saw you standing near the french windows when I flew over.' He screwed the cap on the bottle and turned.

'Wrong drink, wrong time. Wrong place, wrong people.' He handed a glass to her. 'Here's to being in the wrong.'

'I'm not sure I want to be in the wrong,' she said hurriedly. 'Let's toast the right people in the right place.' She tried to smile.

'Right, wrong, who cares? I——' He swallowed the words he had been about to utter and went to stand moodily by the window. Rain still beat against it in a slashing downpour. 'So what do we do now?' he murmured, half to himself. 'Sit it out. Sit it out, boy!' He turned, a self-mocking smile sweeping his face, and half

sat, half leaned on the window-sill, eyeing her
up.

She turned away, unable to withstand his
burning scrutiny, her fingers tight on the fragile
glass in her hands. She took a hurried gulp and
felt the brandy scour her throat.

'Are you sorry you didn't get away in time?'
he asked, voice rough-edged when he observed
her evident signs of nervousness as she began to
prowl the room.

'Yes . . . yes and no,' she corrected truth-
fully, giving him a nervous smile. She came to a
stop at the farthest point away from him,
determined not to go too close. His power could
pull her in from a hundred yards—a hundred
miles—or from the other side of the world if
need be, she thought. Only the picture of a thin,
dark woman at the lonely villa over the cliff held
her back.

'This is going to be a nerve-fraying exercise,'
he told her, making no attempt to hide what he
was feeling.

'You shouldn't have come here, then, if you
knew I hadn't left,' she reproved.

'Are you sorry?' he asked again.

This time she nodded, unable to express in
words all the fullness of her heart.

'I had to come. I didn't intend to. When I
saw you down here I thought, avoid, avoid!' He
tried to speak lightly. 'But my feet have a will of
their own, it seems.' He gave a harsh laugh. 'So
have my feelings, more's the pity.' He dashed

a hand across his brow. 'Is it just sexual attraction between us, Shanna?'

She shook her head. 'I don't—please don't ask me. I don't know.'

'You must know what you feel,' he broke in, tones hardening, face pale in the rain-filtered light from outside.

'It hurts,' she whispered. 'All I know is, it hurts.'

It was the sign he seemed to need. Blindly placing his glass down on the window-sill, he came across to her before she could move.

'I won't touch you. I promise.' His voice was hoarse. 'Shanna, Shanna.' He took a deep breath, all the longing for her welling up, forcing him back beyond the danger zone. 'I want to stop the hurt, believe me. I want to stop it.' He shook his head painfully from side to side, eyes never leaving hers, his own blue like the deepest ocean. 'It is more than lust—I feel a deep, deep involvement with you, darling. A closeness, as if I've known you all my life. It's illogical, irrational. It scares the hell out of me. I can't tell whether it'll fade as rapidly as it's arisen, or last a lifetime, but I know I want to risk everything for it. Do you understand me? Oh, God, Shanna, stay long enough to find out.'

'I can't stay. You know that, Paul. I can't! I daren't!' Her voice cracked. His words echoed her own feelings so closely that she felt possessed by some outside force. It was fate. He himself had used that very word. But it was a fate that had to be resisted.

He held out his arms, opening them to her, inviting her into the heaven within. But the thought of Rowanna held her in check.

'I saw her this morning,' she whispered, voice hoarse with emotion. 'She was sitting having breakfast. She looked so tranquil. I—I couldn't, Paul. I'm not the destroying type. I can't steal someone else's happiness. Understand me, please!' She opened stricken blue eyes, lashes darkened by the tears she resolutely resisted.

Slowly his arms fell to his side, his shoulders sagged, his face became white, haggard. 'You saw her.'

'She seemed content.'

'Content? Oh, she's content all right. Who wouldn't be, with everything they want?'

His savagery astonished her. Grinding a fist into the palm of his hand, he swung away and went over to the window again, picking up his glass and gulping down what remained of the brandy, then standing gazing out through the rain at the deserted terrace. She saw him press his forehead against the glass, and imagined the coolness of it against his burning skin. Everything about him asked her to go to him, to put her arms around him, to soothe his strange, wild anger, but instead she pointed out with an objectivity she didn't feel, 'That's marriage, isn't it? Today, tomorrow and forever.'

She hadn't meant it to sound harsh, but he swung back as if he'd been whipped.

'What would you know about it?' he ground back, his glance raking her flushed face with a flare of hostility. 'Words like that can have as little meaning as the jingles on a card in a stationery shop. But if you had to live with it, minute after minute, year after year—would you be so smug then?'

Silence widened between them. As if it had turned into a physical force, it seemed to send him back towards the french windows on the far side of the room. With a smile twisting his face, he gave her one last dark, despairing look before striding out into the rain.

His name sprang to her lips, hammering in her skull to be uttered, but she refused to call him back. Was his reaction unexpected? For her it was. She thought he was different from the sort of men who wanted the advantages of marriage but none of the restraints. He had slid down in her estimation. But her heart still bled for him. And, foolish though it was, she would have tried to forgive him, tried to make him see things more fairly, if only she'd had the chance.

They didn't meet until after dinner. Presumably he had dined with his wife. The thought was like a knife through her heart. But she had to bear it. She felt quite stoical by the time he reappeared, able to keep him at a distance, but relieved to find that Katerina and Arthur had every intention of staying around, as on the previous evening.

By now the wind was howling around the villa, making the shutters bang, tossing the terrace furniture about in disarray before Paul and Arthur together lugged the heavy things indoors.

'Is Rowanna alone this evening?' she asked when Katerina, suggesting a game of bridge, went to get the cards from a drawer in the card-table.

'Alone? No, why should she be?' It was Paul. He had scarcely looked at her since he came in, but now his eyes narrowed, flicking over her and away as if he didn't want to see her.

Shanna let the matter rest. Obviously he was going to be unforthcoming. She partnered Arthur and felt some satisfaction that they won the first rubber.

'What's the forecast like?' asked Paul a little later after the game had progressed with equal scores on either side.

'Switch on the radio,' suggested Arthur, looking at his watch. 'Worried about Paris?'

'Worried about getting Shanna back in time for her connection at Malaga,' he replied shortly. He dealt the next hand. Shanna frowned over her cards. Now he was savagely eager to get rid of her. She had failed to be taken in by his show of emotion, so now he wanted her to be gone.

'The sooner I can leave, the better. I have

to get that flight,' she announced, looking worried, her eyes darting to Paul's face to see if he noticed.

Arthur unwittingly helped out. 'Have to be back home, do you? Work and boyfriend waiting with eager impatience?' he laughed. 'You can always ring and let them know if you miss it. There's a very good international phone service these days. Not like the old days. Remember that, Katerina? The palaver just to phone to England when we first came out here?'

'I do.' Katerina smiled as she dealt the cards.

When Shanna sneaked a glance at Paul, his expression was blank. He had heard what she said but he didn't care. He looked up with a sardonic smile. 'Mustn't keep the boyfriend in suspense, Shanna. Ring him from the office if you think he's going to be worried.'

'It's all right,' she muttered, frantically, thinking of the two or three casual escorts she could ring if Paul insisted on making her go through with the charade. 'I'll wait and see whether I do miss that connection. No need to worry until then.'

'I'll do my best to make sure there's no disappointment for anyone,' he clipped. 'If the worst comes to the worst, I can even take you the whole way——' He broke off, his eyes suddenly meshing with her own. The accidental double meaning of his words struck them both at the same moment.

Shanna bent her head over her cards, gripping them tightly to conceal the fact that her hands were shaking. After such a show of concentration, it was surprising that she played such a poor hand.

CHAPTER EIGHT

As soon as Katerina and Arthur made a move to retire for the night, Shanna was on her feet. Paul eyed her departure with sardonic amusement, only murmuring as she had to brush close to him on her way out, 'Scared of me?' and raising both eyebrows in a sort of challenge.

Shanna's lips were frozen and she returned one stark, silent look as she went out through the door. Katerina was following close behind, and her last glimpse of him was as he settled back on the sofa with a magazine in his hand.

Trying to shut out that derisive glance, she quickly got ready for bed, sliding under the sheet with a feeling that the danger of being alone with him had been successfully avoided.

Of course, he was partly right—she was scared of him, or of what he could make her do—but the biggest danger came from herself, from her desire to make excuses for him, to reason away the misgivings she felt, knowing that he would seduce her if she were willing, whether he were bound by marriage vows or not.

Sleep again did not come easily. Light from the games-room shone distractingly through the

slats of her shutters. She got up and adjusted
them, but even then she knew he was still there.

Exhausted beyond sleep now, she got out of
bed and went to the window. Should she go
down and tell him how she felt? Try to point out
that, flattered though she was that he should
desire her, he had obligations that must take
priority? She resisted the impulse, knowing it
was merely an excuse to go to him, and knowing
that, if she did say anything like that, he would
have no hesitation in pointing out that how
he ran his marriage was no damn business of
hers.

She could picture his cool blond arrogance as
he said the words, those piercing blue eyes
cutting her to shreds as he spoke.

Switching on her bedside-lamp, she
rummaged in her bag for something to read.
There was only the paperback she had finished
on the plane. Another hour passed. The villa
was gripped in the roaring of the wind, windows
creaking, a door somewhere in the depths of the
silent house banging back and forth with nerve-
tautening irregularity.

She decided to get up to close it, perhaps find
something to read on the way. She didn't need
to go anywhere near the games-room. Sleep was
past now. There was nothing to be lost.

Slipping on the thin cotton nightie she had
brought with her, but without a dressing-gown
as she had decided to travel as lightly as
possible, she went to the door and looked out

into the corridor. A light burned at one end, but
there was no sign of anyone around. It took only
a moment to locate the direction of the banging
door, then she sped off over the thick carpet in
her bare feet, pausing at the end of the corridor
to make sure it was clear. Pulling the door
firmly to, she turned, then gave a gulp of
surprise. A man in a white polo-neck, shorts
and trainers, was walking towards her. He was
shorter than she was, but stocky, with tanned,
sinewy, outdoors kind of legs. His cropped grey
hair emphasised the bullet-shape of his head.

'I—who are you?' she whispered, wondering
if he was some kind of burglar and trying not to
look as if she was shrinking back too obviously
against the door.

'Tom Padget.' He stuck out a hand. 'I didn't
know there were guests.' He eyed her with
interest, standing four-square across the
corridor.

'I'm Shanna Douglas,' she replied. The
name obviously meant nothing to him, for he
merely nodded.

'I guess you're prowling the premises for the
same reason as me?' He gave a brief grin,
indicating the door. He turned then and began
to walk back the way he had come. When he got
to the end of the corridor, he paused. 'If you're
finding it difficult to sleep with all this wind,
why not join us? Paul and I have just broken
into a bottle of Scotch.'

She shook her head, clutching the opening

of her nightdress when she realised he was
staring at the V of naked flesh between her
breasts.

'You're a guest of Paul's, then.' It was a
statement, not a question, but she nodded.

'Beats me what Paul is doing drinking with
me when he could be——' The man spread his
arms in a gesture signifying bewilderment.
'No offence, ma'am.' He inclined his head as if
having read her thoughts from her expression.
'He's a lucky blighter.' His Australian accent
was more pronounced as he said, 'See you
around. G'night.'

Shanna hurried back to her room. Who in
hell was that? she thought. He hadn't been
particularly offensive, it was just the
implication—that she was here for Paul's
delight. He must do this all the time, invite
girls back to the villa while wifey is tucked safely
away on the other side of the island, she
thought. What if she came over unexpectedly,
though—how would he talk his way out of
that?

Oddly enough, Shanna went straight to sleep
when she got back, and it wasn't until Katerina
knocked on her door at about eleven o'clock
with a tray balanced in one hand that she
opened her eyes. The howling of the wind was
the first thing she noticed after the smell of
freshly ground coffee.

'You certainly needed your sleep.' Katerina

placed the tray on the bedside-table. 'I'm afraid
you won't be getting off the island today,
Shanna, dear. You'll have to wait until this
wind has blown itself out.'

'I'll miss my flight,' she observed, feeling a
sense of foreboding.

'Never mind, you'll get another, later one.'

Shanna sat up and straightened the sheet over
her legs before reaching for the tray.

Katerina was at the door before she said,
'Henry wondered if you'd care to join him for
lunch. He's rattling around in that place by
himself such a lot these days. I don't think he
knows what to do with himself since your Aunt
Vi passed away.' She smiled kindly down at the
girl in the bed. 'You see, there's not much to
offer you here, I'm afraid. It must be boring for
you youngsters with no bright lights.'

'It's all right. I'm not complaining.' Shanna
grimaced. 'Paul's wife doesn't complain, does
she?'

'Ah, well, Rowanna has no choice.'

She went out then. Shanna buttered a
croissant and thought about what Katerina had
said.

It was exhilarating to walk across the island in
such a fierce wind, and by the time she came
within sight of the Villa Torres Shanna was
flushed and revitalised. There had been no sign
of Paul. Henry was busy with the water filter by
the pool when she called to him.

He looked up, obviously pleased to see her. 'My major occupation,' he explained jokingly, indicating the filter. 'Tom said he'd come over later to help me fix it, but I thought I'd surprise him and sort the devil out meself.'

Shanna was surprised to find a meal already prepared, with intricately cut vegetables and a mixed fruit salad and a main course of seafood mousse and asparagus tips.

'Used to be a master chef in the old days. That's how I met your great-aunt. She was doing some travel book—eat your way round the world, something like that—and it was love at first sight!' He twinkled at her. 'Great believer in love at first sight, meself.'

'It's not always convenient,' she returned, trying to match her tone to his.

'Convenient? Who's talking about convenient? Love makes the world go round, and damn you if you're looking for convenience, m'dear. Come, I'll show you Vi's library then, after lunch, while I play with the filter motor, you can have a good browse. Most of her books are still in print, but there's a library full of diaries, too, that I'm hoping to edit one day.'

Shanna felt it would be wrong to do more than peep at the diaries, but she spent a fascinating hour or two looking at photographs and the first drafts of one or two of her favourite books. Tom had arrived, and she could hear the two men chatting amiably down by the pool.

'All right, m'dear. You can come and test it out!' Henry stood in the doorway, looking pleased. 'Fancy a swim?' he asked.

'I wouldn't mind.' She got up then frowned. 'Except that I didn't bring a swimsuit over.'

'Averse to skinny-dipping, are you, with an old lecher like me around, I suppose you're thinking. Well, I'm going to be busy in the kitchen at the back, thought I'd do a bit of baking, give you something to take back with you to Katerina. But if you're really a blushing violet there's bound to be a spare suit in the poolhouse.'

He showed here where he meant and then bumbled off towards the kitchen. It was so sheltered over on this side that it was difficult to believe that on the mainland side there was a fierce wind still blowing. Feeling secure in the privacy of the villa, Shanna decided to follow Henry's suggestion. Soon she would be back in wintry old England, and it was silly not to make the most of the opportunities here. She soon found a skimpy bikini and slipped it on.

'Every time I see you you're looking like Venus emerging from the waves. Pity you're not blonde, you could be a stand-in for the original.'

With an inward groan Shanna swivelled towards the voice that had interrupted her daydreaming at the waterside. She'd had her swim and was half sitting, half lying on the shallow steps that led into the pool, her head thrown back to catch the rays of the sun. She brought her legs up in a defensive hunching as soon as she heard his voice.

'What are you doing here?' she asked ungraciously, eyeing him from under her lashes.

'Spoiling your afternoon, by the look of it.' He stood over her, looking down into her angry blue eyes. 'I was going to ask if we were friends again, but I can see we're not.'

'Friends?' she asked scornfully.

'You don't want anything else, do you?'

'Don't waste my time or your own with questions like that. You're strictly off-limits, Paul. I'm not an adultress.'

'My, we are high-minded! Or perhaps you protest too much?' He crouched down beside her and deliberately lifted the wet hair at the nape of her neck and began to stroke the skin behind her ears.

'Don't do that!' She tried to brush his hand away, but he pulled her towards him, grasping her by the shoulder with his other hand and turning her face up to his. 'I'm going to kiss you, even if you think it's going to earn me a thousand years of hell-fire,' he murmured, eyes glinting with amusement. 'You can't lie there half-naked and expect anything less.'

'Paul, if you——' Her protests were muffled at once by the pressure of his lips urgently taking her own in an irresistible attack that left her breathless and angry. 'How dare——'

she began again, but as before her words were cut off by the piratical plundering of his lips, and this time she felt his hands kneading her spine in a whirlpool of little movements that made her swoon with the desire for more. This time, though, it was he who broke away first.

'That's just to remind you what you're turning down,' he told her, husky-voiced. 'Fate seems to be granting us a reprieve, Shanna. You have time to change you mind.'

'Is this the change of mind your whisky-sodden night with Tom Padget has brought?' Pulses racing, Shanna tried to shrug him away.

'Yes, I've just come from the villa. We both rather hoped you'd join us.'

'I'm surprised you didn't want to hurry back home to your wife, actually,' she said as cuttingly as she could. Not waiting to hear his reply, she slid into the water and swam out into the middle of the pool. He wouldn't follow her, she knew that. Not a second time. And when she looked back he was standing on the edge, his face that cool, cold blank she had observed before.

What goes on in his head at times like that? she wondered, heart-wrung despite her opinion of men like him. She turned on to her side. Although she tried to tell herself her path was clear, there was a misgiving like a small cloud bringing doubts with it. She had felt from the first moment that she knew this man. Then, as their relationship had rapidly unfolded, sweeping them both into dangerous waters, her feeling of recognition had been confirmed—it had only been the bombshell of discovering the existence of Rowanna that had blown everything asunder. But Paul's response, his philandering, seemed out of character. Yet she couldn't deny the facts.

He was still watching her, waiting for her to swim back. Deliberately she climbed out on the far side and went towards the poolhouse. He couldn't know how she yearned to understand him, to forgive, to express her love. Bottled up like this, all her best feelings seemed to turn back on themselves, bringing bitterness to her heart where love longed to blossom.

'Tuck into this, then, m'dear. And don't tell me you're on a diet. I know you young things with your fads.' Henry turned to Paul. 'Rowanna's been dieting ever since I've known her. Even now,' he added significantly, handing Paul a piece of apple pie and cream even bigger than the chunk he'd handed to Shanna.

Tom was hovering hungrily near the dish. 'I keep on telling her to put on a bit of weight,' he joined in. 'Make my job easier!'

Shanna accidentally caught Paul's eye and she must have looked puzzled because he said, 'If you don't already know, Tom is Rowanna's masseur.'

'Oh.' Shanna couldn't think of anything else

to say.

Tom gave her body, now covered up under a dress, an assessing glance. 'You seem in good shape. But I'm always touting for custom.' He bit into a piece of pie, cream dribbling down his chin. 'This is a fair old pie, Henry,' he said, changing the subject when he saw the expression on Paul's face. 'My mother couldn't make better.'

'I like to see people eat,' remarked Henry, looking round the kitchen with satisfaction and ignoring Paul's scowl.

'Open that restaurant you're always talking about,' Paul suggested, between mouthfuls. He appeared to regain his good humour and started to chat to Henry and Tom, treating Shanna neutrally now in contrast to that blazing episode by the pool. She felt left out. They all seemed so close, a community. Rowanna was part of this. She was the outsider.

Henry was expatiating on the problems of opening a restaurant at his age.

'We all know you'll do it. It's simply a question of when,' observed Paul when he got the chance. He eyed Henry fondly. 'Go on, admit it. You'd like nothing better.'

'Who'd cook for you then, though, Paul? I hate to think of you living on dried fish.'

'I expect I'd get by.'

Shanna wondered why his wife didn't cook for him, as she seemed to do nothing much.

'I'd miss you, Henry, old man. But I guess

I'll be moving on myself soon,' Tom contributed.

Paul was at once alert. 'Does Rowanna know?'

'Look, I did say six months. I've been here a year.'

Paul didn't argue.

As if something had been spoken aloud, Tom went on, 'If you could only get her to move to the mainland, I'd stick around indefinitely. Hell's bells, man, you know I would. But I can't take another winter here. She knows. I've told her.'

'And still she won't move?'

'Won't, can't.'

Shanna was surprised that Tom seemed to know more about Rowanna's intentions than Paul did. 'Why doesn't she like the mainland?' she asked cautiously.

'Didn't you know?' It was Tom. 'She's agoraphobic. At least, that's the name the experts put to it. There's more, though——'

'Shanna, I'm going to try to get a weather forecast from the coastguard,' Paul interrupted. 'If it's any good, I'll fly you back to Malaga. Have you tried ringing to change your flight yet?'

Shanna blinked. From talk about his wife he had deliberately changed the subject. Why?

'Well?' he demanded when she was slow to reply.

She shook her head. 'Not yet. I wasn't sure

what the situation was——'

'This gale will go on for maybe another couple of days. You won't get back by boat. I'll have to take you——'

'I thought you were going to Paris.'

He shrugged but didn't explain. Obviously he had changed his plans yet again.

It was early evening when the three of them thanked Henry for his hospitality and, failing to persuade him to come with them, strolled off over the cliff path.

'Am I going to meet your wife?' asked Shanna as the white walls of Paul's villa came into sight.

'I don't think so.' Paul halted at the gate and Tom, wishing her a pleasant evening, went inside.

Feeling slighted by Paul's reply, Shanna turned to go.

'Want me to walk back with you?' he asked.

'I think I can manage,' she replied. Her heart was washed clean of emotion. He looked heart-rendingly desirable standing by the gate with his hand on the latch, she had to restrain herself from running to his arms. Of course she could understand now how difficult it must be to be tied to someone who would never leave the island. But that should make him all the more determined never to hurt her in any other way.

With a bleak expression, she managed to tear her glance away.

'I have to eat here tonight,' he told her.

'It's all right. I understand.'

'Believe me, Shanna, you haven't the first idea. Maybe I'll come over later?'

'No, don't. Not on my account.' Explanations would simply make matters worse when they both knew how they felt about each other.

'I'll come on my own account, then. I need to talk.'

A voice from within called his name. Suddenly feeling like an outsider again, Shanna swivelled and began to hurry back alone across the cliffs.

CHAPTER NINE

FEELING trapped at the Villa Mimosa, Shanna could only sit and wait for Paul's eventual arrival. She hoped and prayed he would have second thoughts about coming over, but even so her ears were pricked for the sound of footsteps outside on the terrace. In fact, she saw him before she heard him. Chancing to look up from her place beside the open french window, she saw a tall figure in white striding in through the gate. It was twilight. The sky behind him was streaked in a glory of crimson and purple.

She watched covertly from behind the pages of a magazine she was pretending to read, only looking up with a simulated start of surprise when he stood in the doorway looking in at her.

'I'm glad you're here,' he greeted her after a short pause in which she could plainly hear the sound of her own heartbeats.

'Where else would I be?' she came back, raising her chin. 'I'm a virtual prisoner here.'

'God forbid that any of our guests should feel like prisoners,' he replied easily, stepping over the threshold.

She had arranged it so that he had no option

but to take a seat across the room. She leaned
back in the safety of her armchair and waited for
him to go on.

'Aren't you satisfied with the hospitality at
the Villa Mimosa?' he murmured, raising his
eyebrows. 'I hope Katerina has been looking
after you properly——'

'I suppose you have a lot of guests,' she cut
in, certain he had no doubts whatsoever about
Katerina's efficiency in running the place and
making everyone feel welcome.

'Not as many as I would like,' he remarked,
ignoring her baleful stare and intended double
meaning with an easy smile.

'It must be convenient, having this place,'
she went on, smiling in her turn, 'what with
your wife living so far away on the other side.
But aren't you ever worried she might stroll
over one evening—and catch you with one of
your "guests"?'

He gave her a bleak look, the smile fading
from his lips, eyes losing their glitter of fun,
turning darker, colder. 'One,' he dragged out
at last, 'I don't have the sort of "guests" you're
suggesting—not often, anyway, and when I do
Rowanna knows all about them. And two,' he
went on, 'if she would walk over I'd be overjoyed.'

'I see.' Shanna rose hurriedly to her feet. 'If
you'll excuse me, I think I'll go to bed now. It's
quite late——'

'From anyone else I might take that as an

invitation,' he mocked, his glance impaling her to the spot.

'Don't even think it!' she burst out.

'As I said, from anyone else . . . Are you really tired?' he demanded on another note. 'Or is it a ploy to shut me up?'

Honesty made her nod. 'Actually, yes,' she replied stiffly. 'Surely you must know I've no wish to talk to you. About anything. Least of all your feelings about your wife. It's only because I'm trapped here, like a bird in a cage, that you've got this opportunity at all. And——'

'Oh, do sit down, Shanna. I hate talking to people who hover over me——'

'I am not "hovering"——'

'No, you're too far away. Hovering implies crowding. And that's the last thing you're doing. Come here.' He didn't move. But his eyes held hers, compelling her to obey.

'Certainly not,' she managed to protest. 'I——'

'Come here. Come and sit beside me.'

'No, I won't. I——'

'Shanna, do come . . .' He patted the space by his side. 'Come here, Shanna.'

For an interminable moment she felt the power of his will drawing her towards him and her limbs seemed to have no volition of their own. But a picture of what would inevitably follow when he put his arms around her made her bring all her resistance to bear. With a toss of her head, she plumped abruptly into the armchair again.

There was a slight pause in which his eyes mocked hers, before he said, 'Well, at least you're not going off to your solitary bed just yet awhile.'

'If you think you've won some battle of wills, Paul Elliot, you can think again. I'll give you five minutes to say whatever it is you have to say, then,' she looked at her watch, 'I am definitely turning in. Alone.'

'What I love about you, Shanna, is your clear-eyed view of life. Only possible, I think, because you've never been faced with a moral dilemma before. Not until now, that is. I wonder,' he went on before she could break in, 'whether your clear-eyed approach will stand you in good stead when the chips are down?'

'What chips?'

'You know what chips . . . I want you. I feel something powerful for you. I know you feel something for me—maybe it's only lust, who knows, it's far too soon to tell, but it's there whether you'll admit it or not. And sooner or later, darling, I'm going to have you and you'll give yourself to me fully and willingly. And that,' he concluded, 'is a promise.'

'I——' Her mouth opened and closed like a fish. 'You certainly lay it on the line,' she managed to croak, trying to look affronted. Her pulses in fact raced with a ferocious speed to hear him put into words what she longed for with all her soul. 'Of course, you're wrong.

It will never happen,' she countered, dropping her gaze to the fingers twisting in her lap. Vainly trying to summon up the anger she knew she ought to feel, she took a shuddering breath, but her mind was bereft of the appropriate words, leaving her gazing speechlessly at the floor.

'I know I'm married. It's an obstacle——'

'That's no understatement!' She gave a hard laugh.

'So let's see how you cope with it, shall we?' His mouth twisted cruelly and he leaned forward to say, 'How pure is Miss Purity when really tempted?' His mocking voice scarcely rose above a whisper. 'How strong are your principles, my dear?'

She thought he was going to come over to her and she braced herself for his touch, but to her surprise he remained where he was, just looking at her, that smile, both tender and dangerous, playing around his lips.

'You think you'll test me and I'll fail. What a hope,' she muttered. 'I've no intention of giving in to you, so that's all there is to it.'

'Look at it another way, my sweet baby, not as giving in to me, but as giving in to yourself— of giving yourself what you really desire above all else.' He chuckled. 'And if that sounds conceited, you ought to be sitting where I am. You have the most speaking eyes of anyone I've ever seen.' He paused. 'They tell me what you're really feeling much more honestly than your lying lips . . .'

When she gave a start of anger he laughed again. 'You look so soft and vulnerable, Shanna, I do adore you. Your eyes are like great big kitten's eyes, slightly wide with fright, but full of mischief too when the situation's right. I want you to give in to that playful nature of yours, enjoy it, Shanna, while you've got youth and health and beauty, because otherwise one day you'll wake up and find it all gone and you'll be left with nothing but yearnings for what might have been, and believe me, that's the saddest feeling in the world . . .'

'If you think you can seduce me with words, Paul, you're in for a grave disappointment,' she argued, glancing up quickly and away again. It was as if she had been tied to the chair. She couldn't have got up and walked out if she'd tried.

'There, that little frightened kitten look— it makes me want to protect you, to hold you, dear, sweet creature, and keep you safe from harm. Trust me, Shanna. Let me take care of you.'

'As your mistress?'

'To begin with.'

'You mean you're going to use that old ploy?'

'Which one?' He looked interested, his eyes sharpening.

'The one men always use. Be my little playmate, please, followed by a promise of something more permanent in the future. A promise never to be kept. Just like your marriage vows——'

'That's a ploy you've come across often, is it?' he asked, a flash of anger roughening his tone.

'Not personally.' She tossed her head as if to say, Would she be so gullible? and went on, 'But I'm not so ignorant that I don't know what men say in order to get their own way——'

'You're so sweet.' His anger was quickly replaced by the familiar bantering smile. 'Does all your knowledge come from cheap magazines?'

'Not at all!' she replied, cheeks flushing hotly. It was true she felt the gap in her experience and sometimes wondered if she appeared naïve. Paul had obviously done a lot more living than she had. So, too, had Rowanna, judging by the photograph. They lived in the fast stream, jet-set, cosmopolitan. She was out of her depth here and she knew it.

'Let me go, Paul. What possible satisfaction can you get from seducing someone against their will?'

'I don't intend to. I merely want you to discover your will. To be yourself. Not some clone, pieced together from half-truths and puritanical inhibitions.'

'Perhaps that's the real me,' she suggested

coldly, wishing he wouldn't try to put doubts in her head.

'Is it?' He laughed softly. 'I have reason to think differently.'

'No reason,' she flared, 'except your own lustful wishes! Well, keep wishing, because you'll never get me round to your way of thinking!'

'Let's have some music,' he suddenly suggested, getting to his feet and going over to the elaborate stereo. 'What do you like?'

'Anything,' she muttered, glad that the conversation had taken a change of direction. She watched him riffle along the shelves of discs, finally selecting one and slipping it on to the turntable with a little smile playing around his lips.

'Now, that's better,' he said as the mellow chords of a guitar filled the room. 'Maybe it'll help you relax,' he suggested, going over to his own chair again and lolling back with his eyes closed and a look of contentment on his face.

Shanna let the music wash over her in a seductive murmur of sound, wishing he had chosen something less romantic and knowing full well that it had been a deliberate choice. Yet now he seemed to be drifting off in a world of his own, scarcely aware that she was sitting, not at all relaxed, only yards away.

Her own thoughts began to drift under the influence of the music, mingling haphazardly with the words of the song. It was something about a girl sitting at a window looking out at the world as it passed her by. A Lady of Shalott theme, she registered, and maybe Paul is trying to say something to me through the song. He seems to think I get all my experience second-hand, through a distorting mirror of false morality. But am I watching the world go by, keeping a safe distance? Uninvolved? Aloof? Just because I say no doesn't mean I don't feel . . . I really can't say yes. There's Rowanna. And she needs him. She must do. It's unfair of him to feel bored or irked because she's ill. That's what marriage means: for better, for worse, in sickness and in health.

She looked across at him and blushed to find his eyes fixed intently on her face.

'Is it the legal fact of marriage that bothers you, Shanna, or the thought that I might be sleeping with her?' His lips scarcely moved. She had to check to make sure she hadn't imagined the sound of his voice. He raised an eyebrow when she didn't reply straight away. 'Well, which?'

She took a gulp of air. 'I thought you were asleep,' she hedged.

'As you see, I'm not, so don't avoid the question.'

'I'm not avoiding it. And you must know the answer—I mean, it's both, isn't it? I believe that if you make a promise you should keep it. Nothing would work if nobody kept their word.'

'Do you think I don't agree with you? But it works both ways, you know. If somebody breaks an agreement with you, that invalidates your agreement with them, doesn't it?'

She bit her lip. 'It would depend on circumstances.'

'I see.' He smiled without humour. 'At least your principles aren't as inflexible as they seem.' He paused. 'You must have realised Rowanna and I don't sleep together any longer.' He quirked an eyebrow.

Shanna flushed. How could his wife keep her hands off him?

'What was the thought that flashed through your mind just then?' he demanded, eyes lazing over her sprawling body in a way that made her draw up her knees in self-defence. She tried to make it look as if she was changing one relaxed posture for another.

'I wasn't really thinking of anything,' she fibbed.

'Leaving it to my imagination, are you? Dangerous ploy, my sweet. You know what my imagination is like when you're around.'

'As long as your thoughts stay firmly where they belong,' she replied, trying to look casual.

'Did you realise we weren't together in that sense any longer?' he insisted.

She shook her head. 'It doesn't really alter the situation. Obviously she needs you. I don't know much about agoraphobia, but it must make her feel pretty helpless.'

'Must it?' His eyes were bleak again, chips of
blue ice glittering in the light from the floor
lamp by his chair. 'You know nothing, Shanna.
Nothing.'

'Then why don't you enlighten me?' she
prompted. 'Isn't that why you came over, to
talk to me? To see if you can persuade me to
see things your way? But of course,' she went
on, 'you don't really need to put it into words at
all, do you? Naïve and inexperienced as I am, I
think I know how this particular line goes. It's
something like this,' and, taking a deep breath,
she began to talk with mock sincerity, saying,
'my wife doesn't really understand me and of
course we never sleep together. I know you
understand me, I can see it in your eyes. Of
course I can't go into detail, it's too painful,
but I'm sure you'll sympathise with me and give
me what I want——'

'Shut up! Just shut up!' His face was stark
white, and what had begun as a malicious
parody, a self-defensive measure, elicited an
outburst that stunned Shanna into momentary
silence.

'You don't understand. I don't expect you to.
And I'm emphatically not going to explain
anything to you when you're in this mood!'

'Then don't!' she sparked back when she'd
recovered. 'Do you imagine I'm interested? Go
to hell! You and your wife, both! Plus whatever bedtime arrangements you happen to

have!'

He leaned forward and reached for her wrist, yanking her roughly towards him so she was jerked down off the edge of the chair on to her knees, then he was leaning over her, his words hissing explosively into her ears. 'Stop behaving like a silly, stupid schoolgirl, Shanna. Show some understanding, can't you? Do you think I'm completely insincere? All right, I want to make love to you, and yes, I'm a man, and if I can tease you or cajole you into bed with me, I will, make no mistake. But I don't lie to you, Shanna. I've never lied to get a woman to love me. I mean everything I say. What I will not do is spin you some story to make you come to me for the wrong reasons. I don't want your pity, your sympathy, your moral judgements. You'll come to me despite your second-hand principles because you'll be driven into my arms by love and desire and overwhelming need. I won't have you under any other terms. But by God,' he paused, 'I know I could take you any time I chose if I was the type of man you seem to think I am.'

He still held her by both wrists and he massaged them gently as if to emphasise his words. 'Do you imagine I'm so inexperienced I couldn't play you like a fish on a line?' His glance held hers and he went on, 'But that's the last way I want to take you.' His voice dropped to a whisper. 'When you come to me you're going to be aware of what you're doing, and if it's a choice between your schoolgirl morality and me, hell, it's going to be me you choose. Understand?'

His face was chalk-white, inches from her own. She felt the surface of her skin yearn for his caress, but something hard resisted him and she fought to get away, surprised when he released his grip as abruptly as it had been imposed.

'I'll never give up what I believe is right. No matter how——' she fumbled for the words that wouldn't make him think she was about to yield, 'however domineering you are,' she stated, finding one that seemed right. 'You'll find I won't be bullied,' she added. 'Not everybody can be. And I can't! I won't!'

'Bullied? You don't know anything about bullying,' he told her. 'You don't imagine my grabbing your wrists constitutes bullying, do you? Bullying, dear child, on its more subtle level, involves wielding the stick and carrot of moral blackmail. You're an innocent, luckily, when it comes to that.' He seemed as if he was about to go on, and Shanna got the strongest feeling there was much more behind his words than appeared at face-value. He sounded as if he was hinting at some deep personal experience.

She gave him a sharp glance. 'I can't imagine anybody getting far with the carrot and stick approach with you,' she muttered, surprised when he rolled his eyes to the ceiling.

'One day, when there's nothing to be gained from telling you, you'll get the truth, the pure, unvarnished and horrid truth.' He spoke humorously, but again Shanna caught a fleeting glimpse of that bleak, blank, shuttered look with which he preserved his emotional privacy.

'That'll be the day.' She scrambled back on to the chair and pulled her skirt down over her knees. The record came to a stop.

'Is that what you want on next?' He hummed a few bars of the Buddy Holly number. 'Or would you prefer something a little more late-night?'

She caught his glance and almost smiled. He was teasing her and he looked irresistible like that, blue eyes bright and that sun-bleached hair rumpled from where he'd been lying back on the sofa.

'It must be easy for a man like you. You just click your fingers and the girls come running.' She gave him a knowing look.

'Well,' he said, his glance holding hers, 'you can't win 'em all!' He put another record on the turntable and Shanna bit her lip. It was one of her favourite smoochy melodies, and until now there had been no particular man in mind whenever she heard it. From this day on she knew it would always remind her of Paul, of what might have been. What if he's right? she thought suddenly. What if I regret saying no in a year or two? There'll never be anyone else like him.

Her glance darted to where he was standing over by the window. He seemed reluctant to come and sit down, and with his face averted she could only guess at his mood. Something about the way his head was bent made her long to comfort him. But it was always the same thing holding her back. Despite what he had told her about Rowanna, she still felt it would not be right to unveil her true feelings. She had no right to do it.

He lifted his head, swinging right round to look at her. 'I guess this will always be our song, Shanna. Whether fate brings us together or not.'

She shuddered at how similar their thoughts had been, and he must have noticed the sudden revelation of what lay deepest in her heart before she turned away and pretended to smooth her skirt, for he said softly, 'I know, sweetheart, I know,' moving towards her with the silence of a cat, adding, 'It's hard, isn't it? Treading the straight and narrow?'

Hardly daring to look up, she could feel him standing over her, tall and powerful.

'Second thoughts? There's still time. The wind seems to be dropping, and when it does I shall have run out of excuses to keep you here any longer.'

'I must get back as soon as I can——' she explained hurriedly.

'To the boyfriend . . .'

'You know there's no one,' she told him,

raising her eyes. 'How could there be, now I've
met you?' Her eyes glistened. There was so
little time. He was right about that. Soon the
chance would be gone forever and she could
almost taste the regret on her tongue. 'Oh,
Paul! I can't bear the thought of never——' she
took a deep, shuddering breath, plunging on
recklessly with, 'the thought of never seeing you
again.'

It was like the time she'd told him she thought
she loved him. But this time the feeling was
deeper. It was tried and tested. She had learned
things about him which she would rather not
know. Romance had been tempered with
reality. But it still rushed her headlong into
confessing her most heartfelt emotions. They
were the same. To love once was to love forever.

Bending down, he took both her hands in his
and held them, carefully and caringly drinking
in the sight of her upturned face, with its wide,
wild fawn-eyes, the generous mouth made for
loving and kissing, and the pale porcelain skin,
blushing now with the power of the shared
feelings hurtling between them.

'It would take a saint to resist you, Shanna,
and I'm no saint . . .' His grip tightened in a
convulsion of desire scarcely reined in. 'Will
you hate me if—tomorrow . . .' Instead of
words, the thumb of one hand began to create
little circles of pleasure inside the curled palm
resting in his. Time seemed to expand like

a bubble, enclosing them in a private world of touch, and somehow his arms were sliding around her, drawing her close into his protection, lips muffling into her dark hair, making her skin blaze with the premonition of what it would be like to be loved completely.

Before she could answer a voice from the terrace transfixed them to the spot.

'So there you are,' it rasped with undisguised venom. 'I might have guessed!'

As if she was having a bad dream, Shanna lifted her head from Paul's shoulder to find her startled glance riveted by the sight of a furious thin face gazing in at them from the terrace. Dark hair hung around the woman's shoulders, blown in disarray by the night wind, her eyes, glittering with hate, boring into Shanna's love-bleared ones.

Slowly, as if it was physical pain to separate, they moved apart, linked only by his hand still grasping her tightly around the waist.

It burned with the guilt of something forbidden under the possessive eye of his wife.

'What are you doing here?' he asked dully, as if finding it difficult to make sense of her presence.

'Sorry to surprise you, darling!' she spat. 'How sad! Next time you're entertaining one of your whores, perhaps you'll warn me?'

With a sound like a snarl issuing from between her teeth, she spun furiously and ran off into the darkness.

'Rowanna!' Paul dropped his hand from round Shanna's waist and took two strides towards the terrace before coming to a halt. Slowly he spun to face her. For a moment silence hung between them.

Then Shanna found her voice. With a contemptuous look at his ashen face, she said, 'So you'd be overjoyed if she ever came up here, would you, Mr Elliot? I can see that. Your delight is obvious!'

Then, with as much dignity as she could display, she spun on her heel and, forcing herself not to run, walked straight from the room.

As she turned to close the door behind her, she saw Paul stand for a moment, then, with a kind of curse, he plunged off into the night after the fleeing figure of his wife.

CHAPTER TEN

As Paul had observed, the wind was beginning to drop, and by morning it had disappeared altogether, leaving a glittering sun dancing on the calmest of blue seas. Once again the air was fresh and clear, the island at its most beautiful.

Shanna, dry-eyed, finished her packing and stood for one last time at the window, gazing out at the elegant curve of the terrace, the turquoise pool, the picture-book palms.

Soon she would be gone for good.

Making sure everything was as she had found it, she picked up her bag and left the room.

Arthur had told her that the mail-boat would be passing as soon as the weather improved. Now, with a hastily scribbled thank-you note to Katerina and a promise to them both that she would sign over the bill of sale as soon as her solicitor in London had had a look at it, she made her way as quietly as she could to the small harbour where she had been dropped off a lifetime ago.

Her departure went unnoticed, and soon she was hitching a lift on the back of a petrol bike driven by a young man she met on the boat, and after that it was the bus from Santa Eulalia to

the main port, another ferry, another bus, and
then, at last, a stand-by back to Heathrow.

It was dawn by the time she looked down over
the endless roofs of London's suburbs as the
plane homed in through random cotton-wool
clouds, and she couldn't help feeling that her
own searing unhappiness must be reflected a
thousand times in the hearts of the tiny
inhabitants she could see scurrying about
below. But it didn't make the agony any the
less.

In the Ladies she noticed with surprise how
fresh-faced she looked; pale, perhaps, eyes a
little darker than usual, but cool, composed, lips
as always seeming to curve ready for laughter.
How deceptive appearances are, she thought
wryly, feeling a shudder of nausea wrench her
guts when the thought she was fighting to keep
at bay slammed through her yet again. Quickly
drying her hands, she hurried out into the
concourse. As soon as she was safely back home
she need never think of Spain again. Once she
was back in the thick of things at work, Paul
would rapidly become a memory, as
insubstantial as the holiday snapshots that
decorated the walls of the office.

Needless to say, he hadn't returned that night
after the dreadful intrusion by his wife, and it
was obvious what interpretation she was
supposed to put on that. Nothing could be
clearer. But it hadn't been like that, she told
herself, hurrying through the concourse. It

hadn't been like that for her. What Paul thought would be reflected in the views of his wife. That hurt. But she knew her own integrity was intact. As for trusting him—she'd shown the folly of trusting him; now she would never trust again.

She had been back five days when a letter arrived with a Parisian postmark. It was from Paul, and he simply said he would be in London towards the end of the month, naming a specific date. Shanna promptly arranged to be out of town, and when she returned on the Monday morning there was a single long-stemmed rose on the doormat and a terse card: 'Where were you?' with his sprawling signature which she had seen only once before. She stared at it for a long time, wondering how a handwriting expert would analyse it, curious to know if treachery could be detected in the sloping curves of the letters.

Dee had managed to prise the gist of what had happened out of her, though over that last humiliating evening Shanna had drawn a careful veil.

'It didn't work out,' she had admitted, playing it down as much as possible, and now, not knowing all the facts, Dee urged her to get in touch with him.

'There is absolutely no point whatsoever in getting in touch with a man I thoroughly despise,' she announced. 'There would be no

future with him, Dee. He's like a million other
married men—he wants to have his cake and eat
it. Well, fair enough, I'm not making
judgements. All I know is, I'm not going to be
his bit of crumpet on the side!' She tried to
laugh, but the sound rapidly turned into
something too much like a sob and she had to
make some excuse to go into the bathroom.
When she emerged ten minutes later, Dee
didn't pursue the subject.

Three letters arrived over the next fortnight. All
of them Shanna threw, unopened, into the bin.
Each time she saw the familiar blue airmail
envelope on the mat she felt her heart begin to
bleed afresh, but after failing to reply to any of
them and several days went by without one she
felt an extra twist of agony to think that at last he
had given up and all ties were severed for good.

It was Friday evening. Shanna had a long
weekend ahead. Dee was spending a few days
with friends in the country and, declining the
invitation on her own behalf, Shanna had
explained that she wanted to redecorate her room.
Methodically starting to get rid of everything that
existed 'before Paul', including clothes and the
paperback she had been reading on the flight
over, she hoped to be able to purge the memory of
him forever. Now she was going to revamp her
whole image, starting with her bedroom.
   As she hurried along the main road she heard

footsteps behind her, then someone grasped
hold of the shopping-bag she was carrying and,
thinking it was a mugger—though what they
wanted with her shopping she couldn't
imagine—she half-turned, one hand raised to
defend herself. It was caught neatly in mid-air,
swinging her round to face her would-be
assailant. Their two bodies collided with an
impact that knocked the breath from her.

'You!' She would have fallen if he hadn't
been holding her so tightly. 'Paul Elliot, let
me go! I've nothing to say to you!' she ground
out when she got over the shock of seeing
him.

'Tough, because I've got something to say to
you.' He gripped her arm fiercely, glowering
down at her, face rigid with anger.

'Let me go!' she cried weakly, feeling the
familiar feeling sweep over her, weakening her
resolve to tear him verbally if not physically to
pieces. 'I don't want you, Paul! Take your
hands off me!'

His face was taut with emotion, the eyes
storm-blue, gazing intently into her face as if he
wanted to memorise every last detail. 'You may
not want me——' His words tailed off. Slowly
he released her and with space between them
the tension lessened and Paul said quite calmly,
'Let's not stand about in this cold. Can't we go
to the flat?'

She tightened her lips, feeling she should
refuse and tell him to go to hell, but instead she

found herself giving him a curt nod and striding out briskly ahead of him, leaving him to follow behind with the shopping-bag, which he still held in his hand.

It was only five minutes to the flat, and she went round, switching on lights, taking the bag from him without a word, dumping it in the kitchen, then, still in her coat, coming through to switch on the fire, saying without looking at him, 'I suppose you'd like a cup of coffee or something?'

'The "or something" would be preferable. Look, see what I've brought you.' He reached into an inner pocket and drew out a bottle of the brandy they had been drinking the first evening they met.

Without commenting, Shanna fetched two glasses and, still silent, poured a drop into each.

'There's no point in this,' she muttered before he could say anything and as soon as she had taken a sip and felt the liquid fire warm through her. Carefully placing the glass so she would have to think before reaching out for it, she went to sit on a stool as far from him as possible.

Even though she knew what she felt about him, she couldn't deny he was still lethally attractive. His blond hair was the same as ever, with that little bit at the front that somehow always seemed to stick up. And his eyes—God, his eyes, she thought desperately, still the same lazy blue, glittering over me as if he's going to take me and——

'I'm not what your wife said I was. It's not true!' she burst out, desperate to correct any impression he might have that she was willing to give in to him just because he'd made the effort to show up.

'I don't know what she said. She said a hell of a lot that night, most of it best forgotten. I only wish you hadn't left so suddenly next morning. Shanna, don't you realise we could have saved ourselves weeks of hell?'

'What do you mean, hell? The last few weeks have been fine, haven't they?' She raised her chin.

'Have they? Have they really?' His voice shook.

'As far as I'm concerned, yes. Couldn't have been better.'

'Shanna, do you mean that?' Still standing, he came a pace towards her. 'I can't believe you. I'm not going to believe you until you tell me to leave and never see you again.' He paused. 'You only have to say the word.' He paused again. 'Well?'

She bit her lip. It seemed as if everything was rushing away in one screaming storm of pain, all the memories tormenting her soul over the last few weeks pouring back in a flood, a hundred times worse, threatening to go on for eternity in an agony of unbearable longing. If she let him go . . . Her eyes sought and found his. If she let him go . . . She took two paces across the room.

Then they were in each other's arms, his lips branding their message of desire on to her own. When she lifted her eyelids she was astonished to see beads of moisture in the corners of his eyes.

'Paul, I'm scared. I can't bear the thought of seeing you leave, but I can't give in either——' she gasped. 'It goes against everything I believe, to make love with another woman's husband.' She raised her stricken glance to his. Her face was stark white, like someone at a road accident. She felt his hands slip away from her and he was stepping back. 'I can't——' She clasped her hands together and twisted them helplessly. He would leave. He would go forever. She would never see him again. Never . . .

'No!' With a wounded cry she flung herself into his arms. 'I don't care, oh, darling, my love, my love. You're here, and that's all that matters. Paul, please never leave me. Please, Paul. I love you so much. I hate you, but I love you and I just can't help myself. I want to be with you, come what may.'

'It's all right, Shanna. I told you that you could trust me.' He stroked her hair, pressing hot kisses against her forehead. She could feel their two hearts bumping like two animals trying to break free. It felt safe in his arms, as it had always done. She couldn't believe it was wrong. Yet she knew it was and felt she had stepped over into a world where nothing was certain any more.

Her eyes were frightened. 'I know you'll tire of me and go back to her. Oh, Paul, why am I being such a fool?'

He held her face between his two hands. 'You're not foolish, my sweet darling. And now I know you love me. To choose me and forget your principles—Shanna, do you really think I would let you do a thing like that? You would hate yourself within a few short weeks. And then you would begin to hate me.'

'What do you mean?' she whispered, fear that he was going to leave her anyway clutching at her heart.

'I mean, you silly idiot, that I'm not married any more. A state I hope soon to rectify. Shanna, when will you marry me?'

'What? But——'

'If you'd only stayed a little longer that morning instead of running away, it could all have been put right. I take it you didn't bother to read any of my letters?'

'No. I——' She tried to smile, lips trembling, a bewildered expression in her eyes. 'I'm afraid I threw them in the bin. I thought—I thought it would be too painful to read the lies you'd written. I wanted to remember you as you seemed when I first met you.'

'You might have given me the benefit of the doubt. But you never did believe me when I told you it was over between Rowanna and me, did you?'

She shook her head.

Taking her by the hand, he led her to the sofa, saying, 'Come, let's talk. It's long overdue.'

Safely snuggled in his arms, she let him tell her what had happened. 'I was utterly amazed to see Rowanna at the villa. She hadn't been up there for months. It was one of her problems: sometimes she could walk quite happily all over the island, other times she'd say she couldn't manage it and for weeks she wouldn't venture further than the edge of the terrace. If anyone insisted, she would show all the symptoms of a panic attack. It was all genuine. She couldn't help it. The specialist diagnosed it as agoraphobia.'

'But how did it start?' Shanna's sympathies were at once aroused. How could Paul contemplate leaving Rowanna when she needed him so much? She eyed him warily, unable to believe he could treat anyone as callously as that.

'It started,' he told her, 'with a car accident.' He frowned. 'I was driving. She was horribly injured, suffering terrible scars. She's now ready to have plastic surgery, but it was her agoraphobia that has so far made proper treatment possible. She adamantly refused to fly to London to see the surgeon. I'm told there will be no visible signs afterwards. Everything has been made worse by her feeling of wanting to hide herself away.'

'I can understand how she must feel. It must be dreadful. Poor Rowanna——'

'Yes, it's been tough.' Paul seemed unsympathetic despite his words, and again Shanna was surprised. 'The island was the perfect hideaway,' he explained. 'A good place in which to convalesce. But she used it to avoid getting better. Maybe the accident was more traumatic in that sense for her than it was for me—it seemed to make her afraid of people. She wanted to go out less and less. Understandable, I suppose, knowing how beautiful she had once been.'

'But it must have been horrible for her,' exclaimed Shanna again. 'You're not showing much sympathy for her——'

'I'm afraid she exhausted my sympathy long ago.' His face closed up and the blue eyes became as bleak as winter. 'Maybe I'm an unfeeling bastard,' he muttered through tight lips. 'How do I know? I only know what I feel. And why.'

He gave her a sardonic glance. 'How did we get into all this? I've no wish to try to explain about Rowanna or why she acts the way she does. All I know is, she gave me a shock when she turned up like that. She hadn't stirred from her villa for weeks. Then you stormed out before I could say anything. I was torn between two she-devils!'

'And you chose her.' Shanna got to her feet as if to pour them both another brandy, but in reality she wanted to move away so she could think. Sitting in Paul's arms on the sofa was a hindrance.

After she handed him his glass she went to sit on the arm of a chair on the other side of the room.

'This is all very sudden, Paul. Do you really mean you are divorced?'

He nodded.

'It might take me some time to get used to it.' She looked at the toe of her shoe. Did she really know this man, after all? How could a relationship last for long when she had doubts about his humanity? The sort of people she admired weren't like this. They wouldn't leave someone in the lurch the moment they became ill. Especially when the illness was directly caused by their own actions.

Paul's face had gone a paler shade and, throwing back his drink, he rose to his feet. 'Shanna?' He came over, trapping her against the back of the sofa with a hand on each side of her, not touching, but so close she could see the tiny maze of laugh lines around his eyes. 'I'm staying in town for a few days,' he told her. 'I had to bring her over to see her specialist in Harley Street. We're staying at the Ritz. Arthur tells me you said you'd sign the deed of sale, accepting my offer. If you would care to come over to the hotel tomorrow we can sort everything out. At the same time it'll give you space in which to think. I don't want to rush you, darling . . .' He brought one hand up and lifted her chin, then with a measured slowness placed his lips on her own, releasing her at the point where it seemed he might go beyond the point of no return. He straightened.

'Come in whenever you like,' he invited, voice roughening. 'Come to breakfast. I'll be waiting.'

When he reached the door he said, 'I'll always be waiting, Shanna. I'll wait for as long as it takes.'

When the door closed behind him Shanna poured herself another brandy, drinking it with shaking fingers, her mind a turmoil of contradictory thoughts. His coldness was something she didn't understand. Should she be sensible and reject him, after going through such an agony of separation? Or should she shut her eyes to the fact that he had a rather callous side to his nature? If he hadn't told her so frankly about his feelings for Rowanna she would have persisted in her good opinion of him even now, for he seemed warm, loving, caring on the surface. It was difficult to believe he was really otherwise.

Troubled by such thoughts, she spent a haphazard evening doing nothing very much, the need to make a decision, to bring her feelings into line with her judgement, making her restless and unable to settle to anything. Her night was tormented by dreams of a nightmarish aspect, Paul's beloved face turning at one point into an ugly mask, hate-filled and threatening.

Still troubled, she reached the Ritz by ten o'clock. Almost the first person she saw was Tom, complete in running shorts and shoes. He had just come in from the park and, oblivious to the stares of the other guests, was heading across the foyer when Shanna came through the revolving doors.

'So he found you? Thank heavens for that!' he exclaimed without any preliminaries. 'He's been making our lives a misery ever since you left.' He remembered the courtesies then and shook her vigorously by the hand and started to lead her towards the lifts. 'Come on up. He's refusing to go anywhere this morning. I wondered why.'

'No, wait—I—I'm not sure what I'm going to say to him, Tom.'

'You mean you're having second thoughts about him? But I thought you were both—sorry, sweetheart, it was just an assumption I made. The way you both were when you were together. It was as if nobody else existed . . .'

'Oh, Tom, don't. I feel so confused.' She passed a hand over her forehead. 'I do love him. I think he's wonderful. But,' she hesitated, 'I don't know how to put this into words, but——'

'Look. Let's go in and have a bite to eat. It's something to do with Rowanna, is it?'

She nodded.

'Well, if you don't object to my shorts,' he grinned, 'and if I can get past the door, a cup of coffee and a breakfast special should give us time to sort things out.' Ushering her into the dining-room, he added, 'I'm fond of Paul. He's a good guy. But there are probably things he feels he can't tell you yet that somebody else might find easier.'

When they were sitting down and Tom had placed their order, Shanna said, 'But it's nothing definite, you know, Tom. I've dreamed of him ever since I left. I've been through hell. But the man I think I love may not be the real one. Do you understand?'

'I guess.' He grinned disarmingly. 'What you've got to know is that Rowanna is a hell of a woman. She's got me like this.' He crooked two fingers together. 'But knowing that, I can tell you things you gotta believe. You see, before the accident—I've had this from both of them—things were pretty washed up between them. She was a fun-loving girl. I mean, don't blame her, she's got—or she had—the looks. And she made full use of them. I mean, men. You know, they would flock around and—well, she never said no. Now, I can understand Paul's feelings at the time. He's not the type to let anybody make a fool of him. They fought.

They made up. They fought again. Finally he told her to get out. He'd finished with her. He put the divorce in motion, and he'd plenty of evidence for it to go through quickly. But Rowanna still thought she could rely on him.'

The waiter brought their order, sliding the plates discreetly on to the table, and Tom waited a moment until he had gone before telling her, 'She started running around with some no-good guy, and when it didn't work out she ditched him and rang Paul late one night to come and get her out of the mess she was in. In the car on the way home she started bawling him out. He said he'd finished. This was the last time he was helping her out. From then on she was on her own. The decree nisi had been granted and he'd no further obligation to her. It wouldn't be long before the decree absolute came through.'

He paused. 'You don't know Rowanna. She's calmed down now, but I can imagine the whole scene only too well. She hit out at him.' He shrugged. 'It was an expensive mistake. He swerved off the road, and when I tell you he was driving over the ton you can guess what kind of mess the car was in when they were both finally cut free later that night.'

Shanna looked down at the plate of scrambled eggs and smoked salmon Tom had ordered for her without seeing it. 'Was Paul hurt too?' she asked quietly.

'Nearly bought it,' replied the Australian. 'It was touch and go whether he'd pull through. I've seen the records.' He looked away. 'Anybody else would have been livid with Rowanna. It was clear it was her fault, lashing out like that at that speed. But he blamed himself. Seemed to think it was all his fault she acted the way she did. As if he felt there was maybe something lacking in him because he couldn't make her happy. He told me a lot about the way he felt during that night I was up at the villa when you were there, Shanna. It was meeting you that made him rethink the whole scenario.'

'Oh, Tom, he must think an awful lot of Rowanna to blame himself like that.'

'I'm sure he did in the early days. Still does, but in a different way now. He knows they're not right for each other. It was Rowanna who tried to cling on. She didn't like being divorced, being on her own. She kept playing on her illness to keep him by her side.'

'Does he still blame himself for what happened?'

'No, I think he's seen the light. But he still bears the emotional scars, deep down. Rowanna's good at making capital out of other people's good nature. She enjoyed the fact that she'd somehow got the upper hand. She only had to raise a finger and he'd jump. I'm not a psychiatrist, you understand, but it seemed to me that by being so willing to please her, he actually made her desire to hide worse than it was. She was a queen in her own domain. There was no competition. She could do exactly as she pleased. I've talked it out with her. I understand her.' He gave a smile that was full of love at the thought. 'Why should she leave Tago Mago when she could get all she needed by staying put? She must have known that as soon as she was better, Paul would go.'

'Did she know that?'

'She knew. That's why she was nearly hysterical when she knew it'd been left to someone else. It would have meant the end to all her security. She forced a promise from Paul to buy it back from you. At any price. Richard Mather got the impression that the place was worth a lot more than it is, so he tried to get another buyer to up the price, maybe hoping others would come in and push the price sky high. But it fizzled out on him. I mean, it's a nice enough location, but the government won't allow it to be developed, so it's not worth much to anyone in a straight commercial sense.'

'So, what now?' Shanna looked at him, ice in her soul. She couldn't let Paul leave Rowanna. Despite her emotional blackmail, it seemed as if the other woman really needed him.

'What now? What now is me.' Tom beamed. 'Don't ask me how it happened. We just clicked. She's a classy woman and I guess I'm a pretty home-spun sort of bloke. But I'm what she needs right now. And, sweetheart, I'm not going to question it. It might go away!' He tucked in to his Scottish kippers with all the relish of a happy man.

Shanna felt tears build up behind her eyes. 'Oh, Tom, I'm so confused. I love him so much, but I can't get it out of my head that he ought to stay with Rowanna.'

'Don't you dare suggest it! You'll make four people very unhappy if you do.'

'Do you think so?'

'I know so!'

'Oh, Tom, I thought it was just a case of Paul wanting me because——' She looked down, embarrassed.

'Because he can't resist a pretty face? You don't believe it's that any more, do you?'

She shook her head. 'No. And you've helped clear something else up for me, too. You see, I couldn't understand why he seemed so cold towards her. I didn't understand what had been happening between them. It just seemed so out of character—to want to ditch someone when they seem to need you so much.'

'She's got me now. I guess I can handle her. She knows it too. For one thing I haven't got money to spoil her with like Paul. She's going to have to make do with living like everybody else. It's the dose of reality she needs.'

'I do love him,' she said. 'It seems to have happened so quickly. I was frightened by it.'

'Look, don't tell me all this,' Tom grinned, 'tell him!'

She followed his glance.

'He looks like death. Go and give him a kiss. I guess he thinks you're not going to show up.'

Shanna watched as Paul, his beloved face haggard with despair, stood for a moment in the doorway searching the faces of the diners, then his eyes met hers, the misery lifted a little, but there was still emptiness in the glance as it swept her face.

He came over at once. 'Why didn't you come up?' His voice was harsh, making him sound peremptory as if he expected the worst, but Shanna laughed up at him, unrestrained joy welling up, transforming her pale face into a picture of radiant happiness.

'I bumped into Tom,' she explained, reaching up to touch his sleeve. 'We've been having a talk.'

'Look, I've finished now.' Tom pushed his plate to one side. 'Come and sit here, mate. I'm going to take something up to Rowanna.' He got to his feet. 'See you around, kid.' He patted her on the shoulder, then, with a brisk nod and a smile of sheer good nature, he made off out of the dining-room.

'What was all that about?' asked Paul, eyeing Shanna suspiciously. 'Are you two up to something?'

'Merely getting the lowdown on you, Mr Paul Elliot. Do you mind?'

'I do rather.' He began to smile. 'You're looking surprisingly cheerful this morning. Is this how you always look first thing in the day?'

'First thing? It's nearly eleven o'clock!'

'Is that all? I seem to have been sitting up there in my suite waiting for a knock on the door for a hundred years. Shanna Douglas,' he went on, taking his cue from her dancing eyes, 'how about a change of name? I've got one I could offer you. What about it?' His voice had softened, the bantering look replaced by one that told only of tenderness and love.

'I misunderstood you,' she whispered. 'I'm so sorry, Paul, darling. Tom has told me about Rowanna. It's cleared up a lot of confusion in my mind. I just wish I'd known how things stood between you sooner. Dear Paul, you know I think you're the most wonderful man in the world, don't you?'

'That's a good start to the weekend,' he murmured, fingering a tendril of hair on her cheek. 'What do you say we spend the rest of it up in my suite? They have excellent room service. And maybe we can start with a bottle of Dry Imperial?'

'What's that?'

'Champagne, you idiot. It's what they recommend to celebrate engagements.'

'Paul, I love you.'

'The simple words are the best. I love you too, Shanna. These last few weeks have proved that it's the lasting kind. I know I'm going to love you—today, tomorrow and forever.'

And with that he sealed his promise with a

kiss, and Shanna knew that it was a promise she
could trust.

Later she signed over her aunt's inheritance
to him at the price his company were asking,
and later he handed her the deeds back again as
an engagement present. Richard Mather, who
found he couldn't get away from his job in
Malaya, expressed his satisfaction with his share
of the deal, and Rowanna, some weeks after
plastic surgery and looking almost as radiant as
the bride, hung on to Tom's arm and
announced that they'd bought a small villa on
the mainland.

Paul and Shanna returned to Tago Mago for
their honeymoon. Paul had decided to relocate
in Paris, but hoped Shanna would keep the
island as their own special hideaway. They
explained this to Henry, who was just leaving as
they arrived.

'Break your honeymoon for a few days,
darlings, and make an old man very happy,' he
suggested as he opened a bottle of Moët et
Chandon. And when they asked him why, he
announced, 'To celebrate the opening of my
restaurant, of course.' He told them he had
bought a place in the hills above Marbella, and
they promised to fly over for the opening
celebrations.

When they were alone at last, Paul tenderly
pulled the little hearts and flowers of confetti out
of Shanna's hair, watching them as, caught by
the wind, they scattered over the surface of

the pool.

'I thank Aunty Vi for bringing us together,' she murmured as she slid down beside him on one of the sun-loungers.

'It may not have been the wedding she anticipated,' he murmured, smiling, as he began to nibble her ear, 'but who can understand the plotting of a fairy godmother?'

'Perhaps she was cleverer than we thought? After all, everybody has got exactly what they want.'

'I certainly have. I hope it goes for you, too?'

'Need you ask!' She kissed him fondly. 'I always suspected she was a bit of a witch. And she's certainly made magic for me.'

'It's going to be me who makes magic for you from now on, Shanna—you and me together—and we're going to rediscover the land of lost delight.'

'Yes, Paul, yes. Let bewitchment begin!'

THREE UNBEATABLE NOVELS FROM
W♥RLDWIDE

THE COMPELLING AND UNFORGETTABLE SAGA OF THE CALVERT FAMILY

| April
£2.95 | August
£3.50 | November
£3.50 |

From the American Civil War to the outbreak of World War I, this sweeping historical romance trilogy depicts three generations of the formidable and captivating Calvert women - Sarah, Elizabeth and Catherine.

The ravages of war, the continued divide of North and South, success and failure, drive them all to discover an inner strength which proves they are true Calverts.

Top author Maura Seger weaves passion, pride, ambition and love into each story, to create a set of magnificent and unforgettable novels.

W●RLDWIDE

AROUND THE WORLD WORDSEARCH
COMPETITION!

How would you like a years supply of Mills & Boon Romances ABSOLUTELY FREE? Well, you can win them! All you have to do is complete the word puzzle below and send it in to us by October 31st. 1989. The first 5 correct entries picked out of the bag after that date will win **a years supply of Mills & Boon Romances** (*ten books every month - worth around £150*) What could be easier?

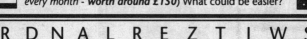

R	D	N	A	L	R	E	Z	T	I	W	S
E	O	N	M	C	H	I	N	A	A	C	C
G	M	U	I	G	L	E	B	N	N	U	O
Y	E	C	E	G	W	H	I	Z	C	B	T
P	D	R	H	S	E	R	I	A	Z	A	L
T	N	S	M	P	E	R	U	N	D	D	A
N	A	W	I	A	T	P	I	I	E	N	N
Y	L	A	T	I	N	A	N	A	N	A	D
N	G	S	T	N	H	Y	D	E	M	L	Q
W	N	O	J	A	M	A	I	C	A	L	A
R	E	L	A	D	A	N	A	C	R	O	R
T	H	A	I	L	A	N	D	D	K	H	I

ITALY	**THAILAND**	**SCOTLAND**	**SWITZERLAND**
GERMANY	**IRAQ**	**JAMAICA**	
HOLLAND	**ZAIRE**	**TANZANIA**	**PLEASE TURN**
BELGIUM	**TAIWAN**	**PERU**	**OVER FOR**
EGYPT	**CANADA**	**SPAIN**	**DETAILS**
CHINA	**INDIA**	**DENMARK**	**ON HOW**
NIGERIA	**ENGLAND**	**CUBA**	**TO ENTER**

HOW TO ENTER

All the words listed overleaf, below the word puzzle, are hidden in the grid. You can find them by reading the letters forward, backwards, up or down, or diagonally. When you find a word, circle it or put a line through it, the remaining letters (which you can read from left to right, from the top of the puzzle through to the bottom) will spell a secret message.

After you have filled in all the words, don't forget to fill in your name and address in the space provided and pop this page in an envelope (you don't need a stamp) and post it today. Hurry - competition ends October 31st. 1989.

Mills & Boon Competition,
FREEPOST,
P.O. Box 236,
Croydon,
Surrey. CR9 9EL
Only one entry per household

Secret Message _____

_____

Name _____

Address _____

_____

_____

_____ Postcode _____

You may be mailed as a result of entering this competition

COMP 6